THE
MAGIC
TREE

**DEVON GARDEN PLANTS
HISTORY AND CONSERVATION**

THE MAGIC TREE

DEVON GARDEN PLANTS
HISTORY AND CONSERVATION

"For what would our gardens be without the Roses,
Paeonies, and Gladiolus of France, and the Tulips and
Hyacinths of Holland, to say nothing of the hosts of good
things raised by our home growers, and of the enterprise of
the great firms whose agents are always searching the world
for garden treasures?"

Gertrude Jekyll, *Wood and Garden*

DEVON BOOKS

NCCPG

First published in Great Britain in 1989 by Devon Books

ISBN: 0 86114-845-2

British Library Cataloguing-in-Publication Data

Devon garden plants.
1. Devon. Gardens. Plants
I. National Council for the Conservation of
Plants and Gardens. Devon Group
635'.09423'5

DEVON BOOKS
Official Publisher to Devon County Council
An imprint of Wheaton Publishers Ltd,
a member of Maxwell Pergamon Publishing Corporation plc

Wheaton Publishers Ltd
Hennock Road, Marsh Barton, Exeter, Devon EX2 8RP
Tel: 0392 74121; Telex 42794 (WHEATN G)

SALES
Direct sales enquiries to Devon Books at the address above.

Printed and bound in Great Britain by BPCC Wheatons Ltd, Exeter

CONTENTS

PLATE 1
Rosemoor Garden, Great Torrington

FOREWORD

This splendid book on Devon plants is the culmination of a year and a half of work by dedicated members of the County Group of the National Council for the Conservation of Plants and Gardens (NCCPG).

We all owe a great debt of thanks to those, for the most part amateurs, who have collated the vast amount of information, or who have illustrated the book, in so professional a manner. The book provides a valuable record of plant introductions from the wild made by collectors and first grown in Devon, together with seedlings, hybrids and cultivars introduced into the county by garden owners, as well as deliberate crosses made by them.

As one who has gardened at Rosemoor for nearly thirty years, and as a Founder Member of the NCCPG (Devon Group), I commend this book most warmly to all who are concerned with the conservation of endangered species and desire information on gardenworthy and beautiful plants from temperate, mild-temperate and, in some cases, tropical sources.

Ann Palmer

The Lady Anne Palmer, VMH
Rosemoor

PREFACE

R ich, colourful, varied and beautiful could all describe the plant heritage that can be found within the boundaries of Devon. Perhaps this is to be expected, when the area of the county is listed at 1.7 million acres (688 500 hectares). The terrain varies from moorland to cultivated farmland and grass pastures, and includes miles and miles of coastline. Even so, a vast area consists of gardens, great and small, carefully cultivated and much loved. The climate of Devon is as varied as its land mass. The peninsula has two coastlines and there are vast areas of high land, rising to 2000 feet (600m) on Dartmoor and 1700 feet (500m) on Exmoor, which attract a heavy rainfall. In general, Devon has a mild wet climate, with rapidly changing variations, due to the rain-bearing Atlantic and Channel winds sweeping across the county. The south coast of Devon is one of the sunniest regions in the British Isles. To understand the reason for the richness of the plant heritage, it is necessary to ponder on these factors, together with soil influences varying from rich red earth to peaty moorland and poor soil, studded with flaked stone or 'shillet'. Thus the county can provide the ideal habitat for virtually every variety of hardy and near-hardy plant.

Apart from the native plants – of which there are a multitude – there are a breath-taking number of 'foreigners' which have come from every quarter of the globe and settled down happily and become acclimatized, over a long period of time. The British Isles depend on individuals or gifts from horticultural bodies for the enrichment of their native plants. Devon has been well served by its nature-loving inhabitants who, for centuries, have brought back plants of all kinds and established them in their gardens or nurseries. Notable plant hunters have been sponsored, and the Veitch contribution is particularly famous and known world-wide.

A great debt is owed to all those who, conscious of the special opportunities provided by our county to nurture the varied and richer world heritage of plants, brought to these shores beauty that is a joy and interest to us all. We can never repay them and can only honour their legacy to us, by vigilant care and conservation.

The British have been described as a 'nation of shop-keepers', but it would be truer to substitute the word 'gardeners'. Market researchers have found that gardening is far and away the leading leisure interest and hobby of the nation. This should – in a perfect world – mean that plants never die out. Sadly they do. So one must consider the causes. For a plant to become 'rare', it could be because it lacks what is known as 'popular appeal'; it may not possess an interesting structure in foliage and flowers, its colour unspectacular, or it may be just difficult to cultivate. Garden centres, generally speaking, are only interested in the eye-catching 'quick sale' plants that empty their sales space and ensure high overhead expenses are met. Only specialist plant nurseries cater for customers who seek out the unusual plant and that means very few make generous profits.

Suddenly, and with a sense of shock, one finds it is no longer possible to locate and buy a much-wanted plant. So much so that the Hardy Plant Society, the Rose Society and others have found it worthwhile to publish booklets on 'Where to Find' a specific plant or shrub. Another factor which endangers plants is difficulty in cultivation and propagation. If a plant needs endless cossetting and care, then only dedicated gardeners will persevere. Others will feel they just have not the time or interest. Climate, responsible for many hazards in plant raising, salt-laden winds, heavy and sterile land, soil that dries out too quickly, all mean that the easy-going plant survives, and the plant with specific needs dwindles into obscurity. Only the plant specialist will give the necessary tender, loving care; the everyday gardener finds it all too much. If a plant is not seen in nurseries, garden centres and private gardens or catalogues and is not widely grown, it becomes a case of 'out of sight and out of mind', and its scarcity eventually makes it rare, forgotten, and sadly, in the end, it may disappear.

The rescue of anything that increases the quality of life is worthy of effort. Although history will show that the present generation has been guilty of appalling destruction, it can also be said that a valiant and splendid struggle has been waged against the threatened total loss of scenic beauty, wildlife and plants. Suddenly, a sense of loss has been felt. Consciences have been pricked and when the media have shown and written about the disaster taking place before our eyes, then right-minded people all over the world have joined hands in a brave attempt to repair the damage, before things that are precious and loved vanish for ever. There can be no doubt that usually there is a financial gain at the centre of the thoughtless destruction. Rain forests and woodlands yield valuable timber, land has rocketing value for building development. Animals have values for their skins and carcasses as well as a sporting potential.

Mindlessly, and with greed, the havoc proliferates. Only by constantly stirring up those who, because of ignorance and apathy, disregard the pillage around them, can the situation be saved – if it is not already too late. So, the few, the very few, compared to the hordes of destroyers with their powerful commercial incentives, try to draw together groups who are strong in their wish to see the world still beautiful and good to live in, and to pass on these qualities to those who follow. Almost all are volunteers and their only strength is their sense of outrage at what is taking place at breakneck speed – the visible wanton destruction of what nature, not man, placed in our hands to protect, guard and pass on. The title of this objective is 'conservation', considered by many to be the interest of 'do-gooders' and tiresome faddists, standing in the way of commercial progress. The endangered world holds landscapes, buildings, wildlife and countless other valued areas of human happiness in its fold. Each draws its own group of defenders who feel deeply troubled and saddened by the threat and destruction.

In our case it is the conservation of our garden plant heritage, and to this end we are its guardians. The National Council for the Conservation of Plants and Gardens was formed in 1978 at the instigation of the Royal Horticultural Society. At that time, it was estimated that over one thousand different kinds of cultivated plants were being lost each year. Today, the NCCPG is a thriving and rapidly expanding organization with nearly five thousand active members who belong to affiliated County Groups throughout the country.

The Council has achieved more in its short life than its founders dared to hope. For example, it has established nearly five hundred National Collections of cultivated plants, thirty-one of which are held in Devon. Each Collection holder, whether private individual or institution, undertakes to conserve a particular genus or group of plants; already many of these plants are being propagated and dispersed among members. This living museum is becoming recognized as a great national resource and a unique institution in its own right.

Perhaps the greatest achievement is the dynamic network of the County Groups, searching and recording, exchanging information and encouraging in many ways the return to popularity of a wide variety of plants.

This book is dedicated to the cause of conserving Devon's garden plants. It has been written and collated by the members of the Devon Group of the NCCPG in the hope that a written and illustrated record of plants with Devon associations will be of lasting value and will help to ensure their conservation. We hope it will arouse the reader's interest in the heritage we value so much, and our wish is to share it with them and to pass it on unscathed and, if possible, enhanced.

Wherever you live, if you are not at present a member, we hope you will join the NCCPG in its work.

Iris Webb   Warfleet Creek
Patron, NCCPG (Devon Group)   Dartmouth

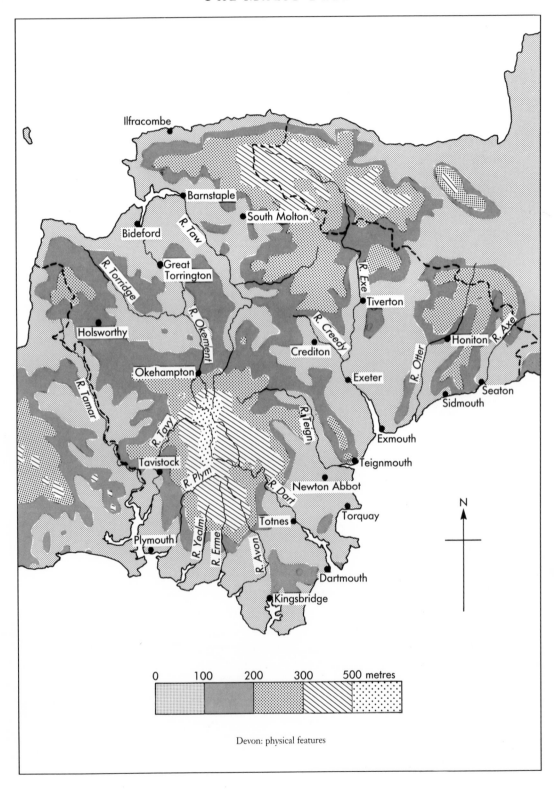

Devon: physical features

0   100   200   300   500 metres

CLIMATE AND SOILS

The Influence on Garden Planting in Devon

Kevin Croucher

T o those who live or travel in Devon it comes as no surprise to learn that it is the third largest county in England. One of the attractions of this large area is the great variation in its landscapes. Over the centuries powerful natural elements have shaped these varying landscapes and these same elements still affect the success or failure of gardeners in different areas of the county.

Every gardener learns that, to be successful, there are certain variable factors that must be taken into consideration. In Devon experience shows them to be mainly: soil type; rainfall; exposure to wind; exposure to salt winds; minimum winter temperatures/late frosts; relative humidity.

Britain as a whole has a very diverse geological structure. Devon represents a microcosm of this diversity. The underlying rock strata form the parent materials of our soils and thus affect what we can grow and how we should manage the soil. A large proportion of Devon soils are loams of one kind or another, but this still allows for a great variation. In the south-east of the county are some very light sandy loams derived from red sandstones. They are warm and easy to cultivate, but hungry and subject to drought in summer. By comparison, large areas of north Devon have much heavier clay loams overlying shale. This can give rise to very cold, wet soils in the valley bottoms to the south of Exmoor. Much of mid and south Devon has the distinctive red loams for which the county is famous. They are in many cases very deep, free-draining and have been utilized as rich cropping lands for centuries.

Besides the texture of the soil, the other important factor to consider is soil pH. The majority of the soils in Devon are neutral to acid. However, there are some areas where the story is very different. The extreme south-east of the county around Beer and Seaton overlies the westernmost extent of the chalk of southern England, giving rise to a thin, very alkaline loam. Further west in the South Hams, extending from the Torbay area to Plymouth, are bands of limestone, representing ancient coral reefs. These obviously have a distinct influence on the pH of the overlying soil as well as providing the basis for much of the quarrying industry, both past and present.

Most areas of Devon have a high rainfall but, as with the soils, there is a considerable variation. The major rain-bearing winds come from the sea to the west and meet the great physical barrier of Dartmoor. This romantic 'wilderness' stands above 1000 feet (300m) and so causes a large proportion of the rain-bearing winds to drop their burden. As a consequence, the west side of the moor has an annual rainfall in excess of 80 in. (2000 mm) per year. This dominating effect of the moor creates what is known as a 'rain shadow' on the leeward side. Successive areas of high ground have a similar effect, resulting in south-east Devon having an annual rainfall which is about a third of that of the west side of Dartmoor, more on a par with areas of East Anglia.

This high rainfall, typical of west and north Devon, has a distinct effect on soil pH and fertility. Soluble nutrients will be leached more rapidly from soils in these high rainfall areas. If lime is applied to the naturally acid soils in the west and north of the county, it will be rapidly leached. Such moist acid soils will naturally contain a high proportion of organic material. The low pH levels and cool, wet, often poorly aerated soil means that organic material breaks down very slowly. In extreme conditions, partially decomposed material accumulates to give us the peat deposits on Dartmoor and Exmoor.

The south-west peninsula, projecting into the sea, creates both problems and benefits for its gardeners. In Devon the north coast is the most windswept area by directly facing the Atlantic, but the whole county is very windy. Trees on high ground in the middle of the county can look as wind-sculpted as those near the coast. However, the deep plunging valleys of much of Devon can be very sheltered by the high, often wooded, hills above them. This can, in turn, bring problems for gardeners. Such sheltered valleys, particularly if on heavy wet soils, can record frosts well into June and thus defy all the descriptions of mild winters and early springs in Devon.

Salt-laden wind is usually only a problem for gardeners within about two miles of the coast. However, in extreme storm conditions – which are certainly not unusual in Devon – salt damage may extend further inland, particularly when wind funnels up valleys that lie in the direct line of the storm. A compensating factor is that in these coastal strips, especially on the south coast, there are areas where winter frost is rare and late spring frost virtually unknown. The dominating effect of the sea on Devon's climate also gives rise to the very high relative humidity that is typical of the county. This has distinct benefits for many

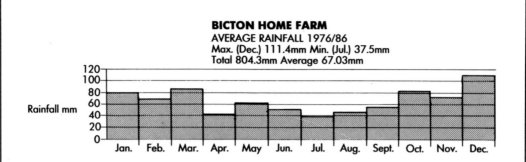

BICTON HOME FARM
AVERAGE RAINFALL 1976/86
Max. (Dec.) 111.4mm Min. (Jul.) 37.5mm
Total 804.3mm Average 67.03mm

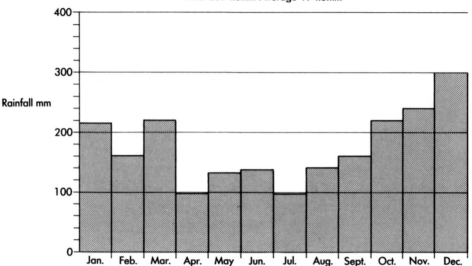

DARTMOOR PRISON FARM
AVERAGE RAINFALL 1976/86
Max. (Dec.) 301.4mm Min. (Apr.) 96.5mm
Total 2094.6mm Average 174.6mm

plants but, at the same time, can cause extreme problems when combined with the typical, but recently all too rare, mild winters. The resultant fungal and bacterial diseases can be a major restriction on the gardener, particularly on certain types of top and soft fruit.

Devon is certainly a county of contrasts and contradictions. Much of what is written about gardening nationally does not apply to our particular conditions. Here, or wherever we grow our plants, the best policy is to look and listen and experiment. Devon is justly renowned for its gardens, so there are a lot of good gardeners to lend us advice.

THE HISTORICAL BACKGROUND

Colin Rogers

With its widely varied climate and soil types, Devon has been an important county horticulturally for several centuries. It is hardly surprising then that a wide range of plants has been introduced to cultivation in Britain either from, or through, Devon's nurseries and gardens.

There are four ways in which a plant may be defined as a 'Devon Garden Plant'. The plants in this book all belong to one or more of these categories:

1. Introduced to this country from the wild, through a Devon nursery or garden.
2. Raised or selected in Devon.
3. Originally found wild in Devon and brought into cultivation.
4. Called after a well-known Devonian or a Devon gardener.

The resulting list contains plants from most continents of the world. There are half-hardy shrubs and climbers from South America; fuchsias from Central America; conifers and *Ceanothus* from California. Australia has yielded some acacias and a eucalypt, and the fabulous Sturt's Desert Pea, *Clianthus formosus*. The best known of New Zealand's daisy bushes, *Olearia* × *haastii*, is another Devon introduction. From Asia come birches, the drumstick primula (*P. denticulata*), and recently, *Cotoneaster wilsonii* from Korea. From the tropical Far East we have tender rhododendrons, orchids, and a range of the bizarre pitcher plants, *Nepenthes*. South Africa has added the near-hardy nerine, *N. bowdenii*, and Cape Figwort, *Phygelius capensis*. These are but a few of the many Devon garden plants.

Devon's hybridizers have contributed much to the wealth of our garden flora. It was here that the first ever man-made orchid hybrid was raised; much of the pioneering work on fuchsias was done by Pince, Veitch and Storey; the first English-raised tea rose originated in Devonport, Plymouth. Early work on hellebores was largely done by Archer Hind near Newton Abbot, establishing the range of hybrids we take for granted today. These trends continued into the twentieth century with daffodils, primulas and rhododendrons, clematis, violas and dianthus. There have been more raisers of fuchsias, roses and orchids. Conifer and heather cultivars have been added by observant enthusiasts, always ready to notice a worthwhile new plant for our gardens.

Our native flora in Devon has yielded several garden plants, distinct forms worthy of cultivation. This is particularly true of a host of ferns, along with a fine double primrose, *Primula vulgaris* 'Pridhamsleigh'. Finally, there are those plants named after well-known Devonians or Devon gardeners. Most of this small group are also Devon raised, like *Camellia* 'Mildred Veitch', which was named after the last member of that great horticultural family to be involved in the Devon branch of the famous nursery. However, *Cistus* 'Anne Palmer', although raised in Kent, was called after one of Devon's best-known and most respected gardeners and plantswomen, the Lady Anne Palmer of Rosemoor.

Probably the oldest of all the Devon garden plants is the Plymouth strawberry, *Fragaria vesca* var. *fructu hispida*, which was discovered in a Plymouth garden by John Tradescant in 1627. This curious little plant still exists and is now arousing renewed interest among plantsmen and lovers of the unusual. It is good to think that it has been cherished for so long by generations of enthusiasts.

However, the greatest period for the introduction of new plants was, undoubtedly, from the early nineteenth to the early twentieth century when great nurseries sent out collectors across the world, with the sole purpose of introducing new plants to Britain and Europe. This, in turn, gave opportunities for the hybridizers to practise their skills as never before. Once again, Devon had an important role to play, largely through the work of two nurseries in the Exeter area, pre-eminently that of Veitch's nursery in the Victorian era.

The first of Exeter's notable nurseries was William Lucombe's at St Thomas, founded in 1720. William's most famous introduction was the Lucombe Oak, *Quercus* × *hispanica* 'Lucombeana', a chance seedling found in the nursery. Although rarely seen today, this fine tree was highly rated and both widely propagated and planted by the end of the eighteenth century. By the early 1800s the nursery had produced two notable apple varieties, 'Lucombe's Pine' and 'Lucombe's Seedling'.

The nursery became Lucombe, Pince & Co. in the 1820s, when Robert Taylor Pince joined the already established firm of John Lucombe & Son. The range of plants grown continued to expand and other introductions followed throughout the nineteenth century. It was Lucombe & Pince who introduced the first English tea rose in 1841, the Devonport-raised *Rosa* 'Devoniensis'. They were among the earliest of the English nurseries to introduce new plants from abroad. For example, the fragrant shrub, *Luculia pinceana* was named in honour of Pince by W.J. Hooker of Kew, Pince having raised it from seed sent from Nepal. Other material came in from Central and South America, West Africa and Australia. The breadth of the search reflected the huge interest in new plants for growing under glass, a major trend in Victorian horticulture. Competition between nurseries to introduce new and exciting exotics was very fierce. Subsequently, hybridizing was also undertaken; for example, the showy hot-house perennial, *Smithiantha (Gesneria)* 'Exoniensis' was raised by Pince about 1869. The nursery was also among the first to hybridize fuchsias, from the 1840s until its closure in about 1890. The well-known *F.* 'Corallina' was among the first, raised in 1842. The nursery continued after Pince's death in 1871, and was reputedly taken over by the Exeter Nursery Co.

Exeter's most famous nursery was originally established by John Veitch at Budlake, near Broadclyst, a few miles north-east of the city. John was born in Jedburgh, Scotland, in 1752, and came south in his mid-teens, where he found employment in a nursery in London, earning eight shillings a week! Sir Thomas Acland, the seventh Baronet of Killerton, near Broadclyst, soon heard of John's abilities and in 1770 the young man came to Killerton to help with the laying out of a new park. By the end of the decade, John had been appointed agent for all the Acland estates. A tree nursery had also been established on land at Budlake, given by Sir Thomas, less than a mile from Killerton, and a house built on the site for John Veitch.

Sir Thomas died in 1785, and work on Killerton park almost ceased until 1808, when under another Sir Thomas, the tenth Baronet, it began again, directed by John Veitch. The nursery flourished and, in the intervening years, work had been done on landscaping parks and gardens around the country, in partnership with John's son, James.

However, the original agreement for the land at Budlake was for the duration of John's life only. This, combined with the inconvenience of the distance of the Killerton site from Exeter, prompted the purchase of land in the city, in about 1830. The 25 acre site of the Exeter nursery was at Mount Radford, on the junction of what are today Barrack Road and Wonford Road. James Veitch ran this new project from 1832; his house still stands on the site, now in the grounds of the Princess Elizabeth Orthopaedic Hospital. It was by now known as James Veitch & Son, the son being James the younger. John Veitch died in 1839.

The nursery continued to prosper under James and his son, and gained a reputation as one of the finest in the country. This later led to the purchase of Knight & Perry's Nursery in the King's Road, Chelsea in 1853. James stayed in Exeter, and was helped by his second son, Robert Toswill, whilst James the younger moved to Chelsea. The two nurseries were run together for the remaining ten years of James Veitch's life; however, they separated after his death in 1863. Thus the Chelsea firm became James Veitch & Sons; James the younger went on to become a leading figure in horticulture and to open more branches of his nursery at Coombe Wood, Feltham and Langley, near Slough.

Meanwhile, the Exeter nursery, as well as a seed shop and warehouse at 54 High Street, was continued by Robert Veitch, who moved from Mount Radford to new premises in New North Road in 1864, with a nursery in Exminster opening in the same year. In the family tradition, Robert was later joined by his son, Peter C.M. Veitch; the firm then became Robert Veitch & Son. When Robert died in 1885, Peter continued the firm. He had travelled widely as a collector, and had worked both in the Chelsea Veitch nursery and in nurseries on the Continent. His particular interest, trees and shrubs, became the speciality of the Exeter nursery.

Peter Veitch received the Royal Horticultural Society's coveted Victoria Médal of Honour in 1917. One of his daughters, Mildred, joined him in the running of the nursery in 1919. By 1931, two years after Peter's death, there was the Exminster nursery, a seed shop in Cathedral Close, and a new main nursery in Alphington to replace the New North Road site. Mildred was forced to sell the business in 1969, owing to ill health; she died in 1971 and was the last Veitch to be involved with the Exeter firm. The company was taken over by the well-known St Bridget Nurseries, also of Exeter. The seed shop was a wonderful period piece, its walls lined with small drawers, each labelled with the variety it once held. It was unfortunately sold and gutted. The Alphington and Exminster nurseries continue to trade under the name of Robert Veitch & Son to this day.

The greatest achievements of the Exeter Veitch nurseries came about through the work of its collectors, and a notable hybridizer, John Dominy. Foremost among the collectors were the Cornish-born brothers, William and Thomas Lobb, and Richard Pearce, a Devonian.

It appears that the Lobbs' connection with Veitch began in about 1830, with Thomas Lobb going to work at the Killerton nursery. He was subsequently moved to the new Mount Radford nursery when it opened. Soon after John Veitch's death, James decided to send a collector overseas to introduce plants directly to the nurseries. Thomas Lobb told James of his elder brother, William, who worked for the Williams family at Scorrier, in Cornwall. He was a competent horticulturalist and eager to travel.

As a result, William was despatched in November 1840, bound for Rio de Janeiro. He was then thirty-one. On his first journey he collected extensively in Brazil, Chile, Peru, Ecuador and Colombia, sending back enough new plants to convince James of the value of the venture. These early collections included several *Dipladenia* species, beautiful pink- or crimson-flowered climbers, of which *D. splendens* was considered the finest for cultivation. This, along with a small Brazilian shrub, *Hindsia violacea*, with clusters of ultramarine flowers, was considered to be a very fine addition to Victorian greenhouses. Similarly prized were several *Calceolaria* and perennial *Tropaeolum* (nasturtium) species; in particular the fabulous blue *T. azureum*. This is both very scarce and difficult to please in cultivation today.

By the end of 1842, James Veitch decided that Thomas Lobb, too, should be sent overseas to collect for the nurseries, to Malaysia and Indonesia. This trip was to prove very productive of plants for the hothouse: various orchids, a range of *Aeschynanthus* species, some tender rhododendrons, and the first of several pitcher plants (*Nepenthes* spp.) were all introduced. Meanwhile, William had been sent out for a second term in South America, this time to concentrate on hardy and half-hardy shrubs. The plants he sent from mainland Chile, and the island of Chiloe, included many of the finest shrubs which can be grown in our west coast gardens and other milder areas. He was the first to introduce Charles Darwin's invaluable orange-flowered *Berberis darwinii* to cultivation. This was followed by the splendid holly-leaved *Desfontainea*, the first collection of the Chilean Flame Tree, *Embothrium coccineum*, some myrtles (*Myrtus* spp.) and escallonias, and the Lantern Tree, *Crinodendron hookerianum*. Added to all of these was the spectacular climber *Lapageria rosea*, with its long, slender crimson bells, which always cause admiring comment. Thomas returned to Exeter late in 1847, William early the next year. By the end of 1848, both brothers were again off in search of the new and the commercially viable.

Back again in the Far East, Thomas collected more orchids, including *Pleione* spp., *Calanthe*, *Paphiopedilum villosum* (later to be an important parent) and the famous blue *Vanda caerulea*. This last was especially welcomed by James Veitch as it proved very profitable; plants to the value of £300 were sold from the original collection. Other introductions included more new rhododendrons, *Nepenthes*, and others. William was this time sent to California and neighbouring states, to collect plants likely to prove hardy in the British climate, but especially conifers. He sent back seed of the Wellingtonia, *Sequoiadendron giganteum*, to Veitch, thus enabling him to introduce this splendid tree to cultivation here. One of the original plants still survives on the Mount Radford site. He also sent *Fremontodendron californica*, a beautiful yellow-flowered wall shrub, and several of the predominantly blue-flowered shrubs, *Ceanothus*.

By 1853, both brothers were again in England. Though they did travel again, little of importance was received at the Exeter nurseries after this date. William returned to California for a final three-year contract and remained there; he died in San Francisco in 1864. Thomas again returned to the Far East, but most of the plants he sent back went to the new Chelsea nursery. However, *Cryptomeria japonica* 'Lobbii' did arrive at Exeter from a small collection sent from the Buitenzorg Botanic Garden in Java in 1854. It is one of several plants to bear the brothers' name. Thomas eventually returned to his native Cornwall, where he died in 1894, aged 77.

The other main collector for Veitch was Richard Pearce. Born at Stoke, near Devonport (now in Plymouth), he joined the firm in 1858, whilst still in his early twenties. He spent a short time at Mount Radford where Thomas Lobb showed him how to pack and send his collections. Pearce departed for Chile at the beginning of 1859. This trip yielded more in the vein of William

A. Baker

PLATE 2
Sequoiadendron giganteum at Exeter Orthopaedic Hospital

Lobb's second trip: *Eucryphia glutinosa*, the vanilla-scented *Azara microphylla*, and the choice crimson-flowered *Berberidopsis corallina* were some of his finds. So too was the elegant white form of Lobb's *Lapageria*, *L. rosea* var. *albiflora*. Another exciting climber was the orange daisy-flowered *Mutisia decurrens*, a plant now barely in cultivation in the British Isles. Pearce travelled on to Ecuador, but foliage plants collected there were destined for James Veitch the younger's nursery in Chelsea. A subsequent trip was undertaken in 1862, also to collect principally for Chelsea. However, he was to find the only yellow-flowered *Begonia* species on this trip, later named *B. pearcei* for him. In the 1870s, Peter C.M. Veitch undertook two trips to Australasia; sadly, on both occasions, his collections were lost at sea. The results of a later, successful trip to Borneo with F.W. Burbidge went to Chelsea, before Peter joined the Exeter firm.

The major hybridizer who worked for Veitch of Exeter was John Dominy, born at Gittisham in east Devon. He originally came to Exeter to work for Lucombe & Pince, but soon moved to join Veitch. His principal achievement was as raiser of *Calanthe* 'Dominii' in 1856, the first orchid hybrid to be produced in cultivation. This breakthrough was greeted with great excitement at the time: the potential for further developments once the techniques were established were obvious. By 1858, he had also flowered a hybrid *Cattleya* and had more orchid crosses on the way.

In 1862 he raised *Nepenthes* × *Dominii*, also the first hybrid of its group. He worked with fuchsias too, having raised *F.* 'Dominyana' in 1852, and others later. His work continued in these and other groups, both at Exeter and, after 1864, in Chelsea.

With the combined plantsman/businessman expertise of the Veitch family, the considerable collecting abilities of the Lobb brothers and Pearce, and the hybridizing skills of Dominy, it is hardly surprising that the Veitch nurseries of Exeter had such a great influence on horticulture in Britain in the mid nineteenth century. The legacy of good plants from these nurseries will be treated in more detail in the following pages. But there are many other people who have been involved in Devon's contribution to our garden flora.

Inevitably, the great landowning families of the nineteenth century had a role to play in the introduction of our garden plants, as has already been seen with the establishment of Veitch's nursery at Killerton. Sir Thomas Acland, the tenth Baronet, is also remembered for his introduction of *Cattleya aclandiae* in 1839. Another orchid, *Odontoglossum bictoniense*, was sent from Guatemala to Lord Rolle of Bicton in 1835, where it was the first of its genus to flower in cultivation. A Japanese conifer, *Thujopsis dolobrata* was first successfully introduced in the 1850s, by Captain Fortescue at Castle Hill near South Molton. An earlier introduction sent to Veitch by Thomas Lobb had failed to survive.

In contrast to the importing of exotics from overseas, another speciality of Victorian horticulture was the collecting of forms of our native ferns. To the enthusiast, the possibility for variation is almost endless and this is reflected in the long lists of varieties which have been named. Devon has again featured in this story, and some of the best of the many varieties found in the county are included in this book; to do them true justice they would need a book to themselves.

Many names have been associated with ferns in Devon. One of the best known was Robert Moule, a nurseryman at Ilfracombe and an avid collector of ferns in the 1860s. His greatest find was the beautiful *Athyrium filix-femina* 'Clarissima Jones', a form of Lady Fern, introduced to gardens by Colonel A.M. Jones, another noted fern collector. John Dadds was also an Ilfracombe nurseryman who gave us *Dryopteris filix-mas* 'Polydactyla Dadds', a variation of the Golden-Scaled Male Fern. From the south of the county, Fanny Kitson is remembered by her form of the Soft Shield Fern, *Polystichum setiferum* 'Kitsonae', found in Torquay where she lived. Other noted collectors included the Reverend Charles Padley and J. Trott.

Apples have traditionally had a strong association with Devon – originally varieties suited to cider-making, later those of culinary or dessert value. It has already been mentioned that William Lucombe introduced two of note. Others have come from across the county; *Malus* 'Peter Lock' was found as long ago as the early 1800s, in Dean Woods, near Dean Prior. Other varieties have been raised at Paignton, Torquay, Topsham, Sidmouth, Hexworthy and Bow, throughout the nineteenth and twentieth centuries. *M.* 'Barum Beauty' was raised by W.G. Davies of Landkey as recently as the late 1970s. Other fruit tree varieties raised in Devon include the Dittisham plum and varieties of the mazzard or wild cherry.

A group of plants currently very popular is the hellebores. Much of the pioneering work of hybridizing and selecting these lovely, reliable plants was done from the 1850s onwards by T. Archer Hind of Coombe Fishacre House, near Newton Abbot. Among his raisings were two named 'yellows'. Regrettably, these are almost certainly lost; however, it seems ironic that there should have been yellow hellebores over a hundred years ago; the few which exist today are considerable rarities, despite being in great demand. This is mostly due to very slow and unreliable increase from vegetative propagation – probably the cause of the loss of Archer Hind's varieties. It is, however, good to relate that the drive at Coombe Fishacre House is still surrounded by sturdy clumps of hellebores, proving their permanence in the garden.

Some of the early work done on fuchsia hybridizing here in Devon has already been mentioned, as Lucombe & Pince and John Dominy (for Veitch) both played important roles. However, William Storey of White Hill, again near Newton Abbot, made important advances towards the creation of the hybrids we know today. Storey worked from the early 1840s until about 1862. He named many cultivars, including three of particular note: F. 'Duplex', said to be the first double, which would now be considered semi-double; F. 'Multiplex', a more truly double variety; and F. 'Mrs Storey', the first hybrid to show a white corolla (the inner ring of petals).

Daffodils have also received attention from many Devon gardeners and hybridizers. The Reverend Thomas Buncombe was working on them in about 1915, at Black Torrington, as was T. Batson at Beaworthy. Later names include Mrs Cobley of Bideford in the late 1930s, and the Champernowne Nursery at Buckland Monachorum, whose varieties include N. 'Red Devon'.

Violets have a close association with Devon for most people. The violet-growing industry based on the stretch of coast from Dawlish to Teignmouth has given rise to the myth of the 'Devon violet'. The market for violet growers was in cut flowers, scent, and violet-scented by-products, such as pastilles. Thus the term 'Devon violets' refers to a Devon-grown product rather than to any specific plant or plants. The only violets which could rightly claim such a misused title are the several varieties raised or found here in Devon, mostly at the Windward Violet Farm. Originally started in 1922 by Grace Zambra and her husband, at Holcombe, near Teignmouth, this establishment was the foremost of the large number in the area. The present tenant, Mr Edmund Holden, is now making an effort to collect many of the plants grown by Mrs Zambra, an acknowledged authority on violets.

Windward was just one of several important nurseries in Devon between the wars. Two more of particular note were the Primley Botanic Nurseries, connected to Herbert Whitley's Paignton Zoological and Botanical Gardens, and the Dartington Hall Nurseries. Whitley's collections were very extensive; from a range of glasshouses accommodating plants from all parts of the tropics and subtropics, to a large number of trees, shrubs and herbaceous plants grown outside in the mild Torbay climate. Thus the listings of the Primley nursery were many and varied. We have three Primley-raised varieties still with us today. Regrettably, a fourth, *Agapanthus* 'Primley Double', has been lost locally and is not currently in the National Collection of Agapanthus. It would be good to find it.

The Dartington Hall Nurseries developed as a commercial outlet for the many good plants grown in the unique gardens at the Hall, created by Dorothy and Leonard Elmhirst. Their wonderful nursery catalogues of the 1930s, illustrated with fine woodcuts, are now much sought after. Dartington, too, has given us several gardenworthy plants. Whilst both these nurseries have long ceased trading, the gardens are, fortunately, still maintained.

The Garden House at Buckland Monachorum, created by Lionel Fortescue and his wife, is one of Devon's best-loved gardens. Lionel was a former master at Eton College, who retired to Devon in 1946. Both the Fortescues lived into their early nineties in which time they created a richly varied garden with a fine collection of plants. Lionel also raised a number of good plants there, especially some excellent smaller rhododendrons. The development of the garden and its small nursery is now in the capable hands of Keith and Ros Wiley. They have very ably followed on from the Fortescues, and are now extending the planting of the garden in their own style, in complete harmony with its conception. The Wiley's hybrid marjoram, *Origanum* 'Buckland', continues the garden's role of introducing good new plants.

PLATE 3
The Garden House, Buckland Monachorum

Several other fine Devon gardens of the twentieth century have made contributions to the list of Devon Garden Plants. The famous post-war garden at Knightshayes Court, near Tiverton, created by Sir John and Lady Amory and their much-respected Head Gardener, Michael Hickson, is one such. Others include: Mrs Ludovic Amory's garden, Chevithorne Barton, again near Tiverton; Dr James Smart's wonderful plant collection at Marwood Hill, near Barnstaple; Sharpitor (Overbecks) garden, near Salcombe – the beautiful mild coastal garden belonging to The National Trust and so lovingly gardened by Tony Murdoch; and the Lady Anne Palmer's lovely Rosemoor Gardens, near Great Torrington.

It is not only the large and famous gardens which have introduced plants, however; Devon is a county of gardeners on all scales. At Zeal Monachorum is an outstanding plantsman's garden of under an acre in size. Terry Jones has gardened here since retiring as a professional gardener and bird-keeper in Hampshire, in the early 1970s. There can be few gardens anywhere of this size which hold a better or more varied collection of plants. It is therefore only to be expected that the plants which Terry has named from his own raisings are excellent forms of their types. For example, in the autumn the terraces of his garden are dotted with many of his hybrid nerines, in shades from palest blush to cerise and plummy-mauve. However, Terry has selected only three of these as worthy of naming. This is in the best tradition of plant raisers; it is in nobody's interest to name and distribute a poor plant.

Other plantsmen who have raised or introduced plants from their Devon gardens include John Huxtable, that rare person, a farmer-gardener. His garden near South Molton was also full of fine plants, from a large clump of electric blue *Corydalis cashmiriana* in a cold north-facing bed, to William Lobb's wonderful blue nasturtium, *Tropaeolum azureum*, thriving in a greenhouse. He died in 1986, but is commemorated by a fine white clematis of his own raising.

Dr Rogerson's garden, Langtrees, at Croyde Bay, is remembered by several distinct varieties of his selection; and a good deep pink form of the Bridal Wreath, *Francoa sonchifolia* 'Rogerson', is named after its owner.

Mr and Mrs F.J. Holmes have named two lilies and an outstanding cool-coloured, medium-sized *Kniphofia* (*K.* 'Mermaiden'), raised in their former garden at Brampford Speke, near Exeter. Mervyn Feesey, an architect with a draughtsman's eye for form and detail, has selected a number of sports and seedlings of plants in his Barnstaple garden, Woodside – particularly variegated forms, and grasses.

It is appropriate that a plantsman and his garden should be remembered by a good plant; such gardens can rarely survive the death of their creators, but at least in this way they are not forgotten by successive generations of grateful gardeners.

Similarly remembered are those hardy souls who have followed in the footsteps of the great collectors by bringing home new plants from overseas, albeit in a smaller way. The Devon Group of NCCPG is fortunate to have Philip Michelmore as its co-founder (with Iris Webb) and current President. Apart from his impressive work as a conservationist and of establishing the role of zoos in education, Philip will be remembered as the collector of *Streptocarpus michelmorei* in Southern Rhodesia in 1937. Likewise, Ivybridge-born Len Beer is commemorated by *Rhododendron glaucophyllum* 'Len Beer', collected on the University of Bangor expedition to the Himalayas in 1971.

Finally, there is the work of several nurseries in recent years to be considered. Burnham Nurseries, now the Devon Orchid Centre, at Forches Cross, near Newton Abbot, has for some years been raising and introducing excellent orchid hybrids for the modern grower. It is reassuring to know that Brian and Wilma Rittershausen are continuing the work started over 130 years ago by John Dominy, here in Devon.

Cecil Wyatt's work with pinks has had a considerable influence. Though he was badly disabled by the effects of polio, Wyatt strived to improve the short stems and split calyces of many older pinks, producing a new race of hardy, sturdy plants suitable for both garden and cutting. The work continues today in the expert hands of nurserymen like John Whetman & Son of Houndspool, Dawlish, whose firm has contributed greatly towards the raising of disease-free pinks.

Barry Fretwell has raised, introduced and even reintroduced some fine clematis from his Peveril Nursery, formerly near Holsworthy, now at Christow. Don Hatch introduced good forms of several conifers, especially *Chamaecyparis lawsoniana* (Lawson's Cypress), from his Chantry Nurseries at Coombe Raleigh, near Honiton, between 1974 and 1986. Trevor and Caroline Wood have named dianthus, phlox, buddleja and others, selected for their garden value. Their nursery, Southcombe Gardens, occupies a cold upland site above Widecombe-in-the-Moor on Dartmoor. More Devon nurseries are mentioned in the following pages; regrettably, space prevents including them all.

The work of many nurseries and hybridizers continues, with more plants being selected and propagated for future introduction; keen amateurs too will find seedlings or sports in their gardens which prove worthy of propagation and distribution. The increasing demand for the rare and unusual has given rise to a new generation of small, specialist nurseries, encouraged by the growth and enthusiasm of the National Council for the Conservation of Plants and Gardens, and the specialist societies. These nurseries are constantly on the lookout for good new plants to offer to their ever more discerning customers. *The Plant Finder*, published by the Hardy Plant Society, is a useful guide to the whereabouts of plants.

Devon's latest good fortune comes from the generosity of the Lady Anne Palmer, VMH, who is one of England's foremost plantswomen and has given Rosemoor Garden, with its extensive plant collection, together with 32 acres of agricultural land, to the Royal Horticultural Society. It will become the 'Wisley of the West', an exciting prospect for gardeners in the South West.

A final promise for the future lies with the NCCPG's National Collections. The aim of these collections is to gather together, as completely as possible, plants of a particular genus, or group within a genus. These plants can then be grown together to check naming (often a problem, especially with large groups of cultivars); to compare similar varieties for such qualities as vigour and hardiness; and to provide a recognized location for study, propagation and hybridization, where appropriate. As a result of the enthusiasm and skill of many collection holders, this project has already had considerable success in its short life. New plants are being introduced from overseas – both foreign cultivars and species not previously tried in Britain. The potential for more introductions is considerable. Just one example from within Devon (where there are currently thirty-one collections) is the group of genera held by Elizabeth and Harold Read in their remarkable garden, Vicar's Mead, at East Budleigh; namely, *Libertia* and *Dianella*, *Liriope* and *Ophiopogon*. Over twenty plants new to cultivation in this country are being grown and assessed within their collections. In time, as these new plants prove their suitability (or otherwise) for our gardens, the best will be propagated and distributed more widely.

The possibilities nationally may be imagined, with nearly five hundred collections already established. It is an opportunity the whole country should support and encourage. Locally, it is one of the several ways in which the role of Devon as an introducer of new plants will be carried forward into the next century.

SOME DEVON GARDEN PLANTS

Terry Underhill
and
Members of NCCPG
(Devon Group)

ACACIA 'Exeter Hybrid'

Sir Joseph Hooker discovered *Acacia riceana* in Tasmania, where he found it growing along the banks of streams, rather like some graceful weeping willow. He described it as "the most beautiful *Acacia* of that island". What superlatives he would have used for *Acacia* 'Exeter Hybrid' can only be guessed.

The Devon plant arose as a seedling in the Alphington nursery of Veitch in Exeter and its distinguished parents were the self-same *A. riceana* and *A. longifolia*, the Sydney Golden Wattle. The seedling was well provided for by both of them with masses of rich yellow flowers from *A. longifolia*, whilst the fragrance and graceful pendulous habit were inherited from *A. riceana*. In 1961 the RHS rewarded its outstanding qualities with their Award of Merit.

Acacia 'Exeter Hybrid' is a medium to large evergreen shrub. It is tender and can be grown out of doors only in sunny sheltered spots, often against a south or west facing wall in the warmer counties. It prefers a well-drained loam or peaty soil. Ideally, a conservatory or unheated glasshouse would be the place to persuade this hybrid to show its true potential. Alternatively, it could be planted in a border or large container and would certainly need protection from frost during prolonged cold spells.

Taken during June or July, a moderate percentage of 3–4 in. (7–10 cm) cuttings of half-ripened wood with a heel will root in a close frame using bottom heat. A mist propagation unit does not give such a good percentage rooting. Since the plants dislike root disturbance, place each cutting in a small pot, using a compost of two parts sand and one part moss peat. Pot into a moderately larger pot when rooted and plant in the permanent well-chosen site before the roots become too intertwined.   (PLATE 4)

ARAUCARIA ARAUCANA
Monkey puzzle · Chilean pine

The purist reading this book might very well wonder at the inclusion of this species in the list of Devon plants, as it was neither originally found nor introduced by a Devonian. Archibald Menzies, dining with the Viceroy of Chile in the 1790s, in company with his ship's officers, was offered some nuts for dessert; he slipped a few into his pocket, sowed them on board and presented five seedlings to Kew on his return. They proved to be *Araucaria araucana*, and one tree persisted until 1892. Early in the next century several nurserymen imported seed, among them Veitch of Exeter, for whom William Lobb collected about 3000 seeds in 1841. The younger James Veitch had been laying out the Arboretum at Bicton for Lady Rolle since 1836, and in 1842 he planted the famous avenue of Monkey puzzles, under the direction of James Barnes, then Head Gardener. Twenty-five pairs of the trees, grown on by Barnes from plants he bought from Loddiges', were planted, and stand to this day. They are the tallest of their kind in the country (since the tree at Nymans, 98 ft (29.5 m), was blown down in the hurricane of 1987) and are a little gaunt, but many have been replaced by young trees grown from seed from the originals, and planted by H.L. Furze in 1977 to commemorate the Silver Jubilee of H.M. Queen Elizabeth II. They stand as a remarkable tribute to the Veitch firm.

Natives of southern Chile and north Patagonia, they reach nearly 100 ft (30 m), with an erect bole, spreading with age into folds at the base like an elephant's foot. The branches are whorled, and densely covered with evergreen, overlapping, spine-tipped leaves, dark green and rigid. These persist for many years even after withering, giving an untidy look to the tree if not kept pruned.

The Monkey puzzle was very popular in Victorian times, and planted everywhere, even in the north-west of Scotland, indicating their resistance to rain and wind.   (PLATE 5)

BERBERIDOPSIS CORALLINA
Coral plant

The gardens of the South West provide a successful habitat for this evergreen climber; elsewhere it is safer in a cool greenhouse. It was found in the forests of Chile by Richard Pearce on his first expedition for Veitch (1859–62). Sadly, it is now believed to be extinct in its native habitat.

The flowers are deep crimson, globular, ½ in. (12 mm) across and made up of nine to fifteen overlapping petals, borne singly on long slender stalks in small drooping clusters. The leaves are thick and leathery, dark green and edged with spiny teeth. It requires acid or neutral, moist soil and a shaded position where the plants can climb from 6 to 20 ft (2–6 m).

Berberidopsis corallina was so named because its flowers have a similar construction to those of the *Berberis*. The plant received an Award of Merit in 1901 and an Award of Garden Merit in 1969.   (PLATE 6)

BERBERIS DARWINII

In 1831, the twenty-two-year-old Charles Darwin had the opportunity to sail in *Beagle* as a naturalist on a survey of South America, which was to last nearly five years. One of his discoveries in Chile, in 1835, was the *Berberis* that bears his name. It was not introduced to this country until William Lobb found it on the island of Chiloé in 1849, and sent it back to Veitch of Exeter. Reasonably hardy, it does best in moist soil, preferably sheltered from cold winds. It grows normally to a height of 6 to 12 ft (2–4 m).

Evergreen, with very dark, glossy, spiny leaves, it is early-flowering, the profuse, small, orange flowers, tinged with red on the back, appearing in May. In early autumn it produces a crop of attractive bluish berries. The plant was awarded an AGM in 1930, and an FCC in 1967.

In about 1860, a hybrid appeared in a nursery near Sheffield, the parents being *B. darwinii* and *empetrifolia*, and was named *B.* × *stenophylla*. It has proved a very successful plant, being hardier and having a more graceful habit than either parent. Many forms exist, among which is the sport 'Bickham Devonshire Cream', introduced by Lady Roborough of Bickham House.   (PLATES 7, 8)

BETULA
Birch

On the shoulder of Dartmoor, above Chagford, Kenneth Ashburner has created a nursery at Stone Lane Gardens, specializing in the natural forms and clones of birches, alders and various ericaceous and other shrubs. The site is south-west facing, moist and peaty, which suits these plants admirably.

Among the plants he has raised is *Betula utilis* 'Kyelang', which is a selected clone from a batch of seed sent by the Indian Forestry Service at Dehra Dun. This was collected near Kyelang in Lahul, in the foothills of the Himalaya; the bark is strikingly white and peeling, the leaves are glossy dark green, and the winter buds are coated with white resin, unlike other forms of *B. utilis*.

Another interesting plant is a clone from seed of *B. pubescens*, from Faüske, in Norway. Mr Ashburner, with Dr McAllister of Liverpool University Botanic Gardens, has been successful in germinating and raising some seedlings of this plant, a difficult achievement owing to the fact that the plant grows well north of the Arctic Circle, and is ill-adapted to conditions further south. He has called his plant 'Arnold Brembo'; it is remarkable for large, sticky, sweetly scented buds, and likewise for the scent of the newly unfolding leaves in spring. The bark becomes white when mature. This is a slow-growing tree, suitable for small gardens. (PLATES 9, 10)

BUDDLEJA DAVIDII 'Dartmoor'
Butterfly bush

Personal danger seems to be of little consequence to the dedicated plant hunter. Certainly Mr Hayles, a retired gardener on holiday from Tunbridge Wells, obtained cuttings of *Buddleja davidii* 'Dartmoor' from an inaccessible hollow on the moor, near Yelverton, only by dint of his wife hanging on to his coat tails!

In its native China, *Buddleja davidii* is known as 'Summer lilac', and in most other countries as 'Butterfly bush'. Both names acknowledge the charms of a shrub so suited to our gardens that we wonder how we could ever have gardened without it. It was discovered by the French Jesuit missionary Père David in western China in 1869 and collected some years later by Dr Augustine Henry. Garden varieties of today are descended from E.H. Wilson's introduction, between 1900 and 1908. The genus is named after the Reverend Adam Buddle, a seventeenth-century botanist and gardener and one-time rector of North Fambridge in Essex. The plant is very variable when grown from seed and for some time was named *B. variabilis*. Over fifty forms have been given cultivar names, mainly because of differences in flower colours, which range from white through lavender to deepest purple.

The chance seedling, so bravely rescued by Mr Hayles, was a distinctive form of this species. Its location in a remote hollow is indicative of the ease with which the *Buddleja* will naturalize itself. This attribute was well demonstrated, after the last war, by the rapid clothing of bomb sites with bushes whose incense-scented blooms attracted Peacocks, Red Admirals and a host of other butterflies.

The Dartmoor seedling was distinctive because of its inflorescence. Instead of the more usual 12 in. (30 cm) long tapering panicle, that of 'Dartmoor' was a mere 6 in. (15 cm) long with a number of side shoots of similar length, giving a stubby appearance to the flower head, reminiscent of a Lilac. The flowers, which are late in arrival, are magenta and beautifully scented. The leaves are neat and the habit remains graceful. It received an Award of Merit in 1973.

All *Buddleja davidii* cultivars respond to hard pruning, as they flower on the ends of the current season's growths. They root easily from cuttings. (PLATE 11)

P. Bowles

PLATE 4
Acacia 'Exeter Hybrid'
at Greenway Gardens, Galmpton

J. Primmer

PLATE 5
Araucaria araucana
at Bicton College, East Budleigh

P. Bowles

PLATE 6
Berberidopsis corallina
at Greenway Gardens, Galmpton

A. Kingdon

PLATE 7
Berberis darwinii
at Dousland

R. Fulcher

PLATE 8
Berberis darwinii
at Bicton College, East Budleigh

A. Baker

PLATE 9
Betula utilis 'Kyelang'
at Stone Lane Gardens, Chagford

A. Baker

PLATE 10
Betula pubescens 'Arnold Brembo'
at Stone Lane Gardens

J. Lloyd

PLATE 11
Buddleja davidii 'Dartmoor'
at Southcombe Gardens, Widecombe

CAMELLIA

Camellias are more usually associated with the Cornish gardens, but there are several good plantings in Devon at Bickham House, Dartington and elsewhere, but especially at Marwood Hill, near Barnstaple.

At Marwood, Dr James Smart has one of the finest collections in the country, grown both outside and in several large greenhouses. From February onwards there is always a wonderful display, and plants may be obtained from the nursery. He has made several beautiful hybrids, chief among which is *C.* 'Carolyn Snowden', the parents being *C. reticulata* 'Buddha' and *C. japonica* 'Ville de Nantes'. Extremely floriferous, with upright growth, it is semi-double and has red, medium to large flowers. It received an Award of Merit in 1986.

The firm of Robert Veitch & Son raised some camellias in their Alphington nurseries, and in 1948 one was named *C. williamsii* 'Mildred Veitch', in honour of the last member of the family to run the nursery there. It has blush-white, semi-double flowers, and won an Award of Merit in 1967.   (PLATES 12, 13)

CANTUA BUXIFOLIA
Magic tree

W.J. Bean, in *Wall Shrubs and Hardy Climbers*, refers to this plant as a 'gorgeous shrub', which those who grow it will certainly endorse. William Lobb found it in Peru, where it grows in the Andes, spreading to Bolivia and Chile. Cantua is its Peruvian Indian name and it is also known there as 'Magic tree'. Certainly there is something magical about the clusters of four to eight 3 in. (7.5 cm) long flowers, appearing in April and May. These are tubular, bright rose-coloured, with streaks of orange-red on the outside of the tube, while the spreading lobes are pale pink, with blue anthers to the stamens. The plant is evergreen, with lanceolate leaves, those on the flowering shoots being smaller and more box-like. Veitch first flowered it in Exeter in May 1848, when it was exhibited at the Royal Horticultural Society and was awarded the Large Silver Medal. It received an Award of Merit in 1905.

It can be grown in favoured areas against a warm wall, but a cool greenhouse is probably safer. It takes well from cuttings and needs turf loam and leaf mould, with good drainage. Let us hope that more people will be encouraged to try this beautiful 'Devon Plant'.   (PLATE 14)

CEANOTHUS

These beautiful shrubs come from western North America and are characteristic of the Californian chaparral, growing in dense brushwood thickets. They are found on dry slopes and ridges, where winters are short, mild and damp, and the summers long, hot and arid. The flowers are blue, a colour prized among garden shrubs. A sunny position and poor dryish soil suits them best and, in all but mild areas, they need a protective wall to their east and north; often short-lived, they are easily propagated, fast-growing and flower well when young.

William Lobb collected seed of several species and sent it to Veitch of Exeter. One of his most successful introductions was *C. × veitchianus*, probably a natural cross, found in California sometime in 1853, which has never been found in the wild since. This is one of the most beautiful of the genus, with large heads of bright blue flowers in May and June. It is a tall shrub, 8–12 ft (2.5–3.5 m) and best grown against a wall. It was awarded an AGM in 1925.

Earlier, in about 1850, he found *C. papillosus*, which grows mainly in the Santa Cruz mountains of California, an evergreen varying in height between 4–15 ft (1.5–4.5 m), with conspicuous warts on the upper surface of the leaves. The flowers are a soft blue colour. This species was originally discovered by Douglas in 1833, but Veitch was the first to flower it in this country, in 1854. (PLATES 15, 16)

CISTUS 'Anne Palmer'
Rock rose

Collingwood Ingram, that great plantsman from Kent, collected and raised many plants including a rock rose, *Cistus palhinhae*, from south-west Portugal. This plant, which he collected in 1939, is closely related to *C. ladanifer* and bears white flowers 3–4 in. (7–10 cm) across. Some time before 1960 he crossed it, at his home in Benenden, Kent, with *Cistus crispus*, which is a densely branched shrub with wavy-margined leaves, the shoots covered in white hairs, contrasting well with its purple-red crêpe-paper-like flowers. The resultant seedling is a hybrid of immense beauty, full of vigour and inheriting the best features of both parents. Its large, clear pink, cup-shaped blooms have petals that are quite prominent and crinkled.

The new plant was named after his friend and outstanding plantswoman, the Lady Anne Palmer, VMH, who in 1987 gave her garden 'Rosemoor' at

Torrington in north Devon to the Royal Horticultural Society as a base for its activities in the South West. At an RHS show in 1960, *Cistus* 'Anne Palmer' earned Collingwood Ingram the Reginald Cory Cup, which is awarded annually to the raiser of the best man-made hybrid resulting from a cross between two separate species.

Rooting readily from soft summer cuttings, it is worthy of a place in any well-drained, sunny, mild garden. It resents root disturbance and should be grown up to planting size in pots and not in the open ground. An unheated conservatory is ideal, where it will grow and flower well in large pots, providing it is well-watered and regularly fed during the height of the growing season with a general fertilizer high in potash. Some plants show a somewhat straggly habit but this is readily controlled by judicious pruning.   (PLATE 17)

CLEMATIS

It is difficult to imagine a garden without some sort of *Clematis*, whether in the herbaceous border, climbing up a trellis or wall or scrambling over and through bushes and small trees. Barry and Pat Fretwell of Peveril Nurseries, apart from running their nursery, are making a garden in a woodland setting at Christow, in the Teign valley, to show all the ways in which *Clematis* can be used. Before settling in Christow, they had come in 1977 from Derbyshire to Holsworthy in north Devon, which entailed moving their stock of several thousand plants each time. Not content with the present range of shapes and colours, they set about breeding and developing the genus.

They rediscovered, in 1981, via a customer, a hitherto almost unknown *viticella* hybrid growing on an ancient manor house in Devon, and from a solitary cutting developed 'Mary Rose'. It is fully double, resembling 'Purpurea Plena Elegans', but smaller and more spiky. The original is a giant with several thick trunks, planted about 1900 and propagated from plants traceable to the 1800s. It is identical with the plant described by Parkinson in 1629 as "a double 'Virgin's Bower' of a dull and sad blewish purple". The Fretwells felt that a more suitable name, bearing in mind the coincidence of its resurgence with that of Henry VIII's sunken flagship, would be 'Mary Rose'. A plant is now grown by the Queen Mother at Royal Lodge, Windsor.

The list of hybrids selected and raised by this small family nursery is prodigious and the present selection of yet unnamed seedlings, arising from many enterprising crosses, promises well for the future. The list at the end of this book covers many of their plants although special mention should be made of a *C. texensis* hybrid 'The Princess of Wales'. It is from the cross *C. texensis* × 'Bee's Jubilee' which is not an easy one to make: *texensis* is tubular and tender, 'Bee's Jubilee' is large-flowered, soft mauve-pink with a brilliant carmine centre bar to the petals. Her Royal Highness gave permission for the naming of the new hybrid, which is a deep luminous pink with a prominent tuft of creamy-yellow stamens.

Other clematis growers include John Huxtable, a farmer, who in the mid 1960s introduced, from his South Molton garden, a chance seedling, named after him, which is free-flowering, compact and pure white; the large blooms, produced from July to August, have green stamens in the centre. (PLATES 18, 19, 20)

CORNUS NUTTALLII 'Portlemouth'
Pacific dogwood

The sheltered south-facing hillsides along the Salcombe estuary enjoy a special micro-climate, which the late Dr Barker and his wife used to full advantage to create a garden of beautiful, rare and tender plants at Casa di Sole, East Portlemouth. Protection was still needed from gales and many new close plantings, combined with the clever use of existing trees, enabled shrubs and smaller plants to grow quickly.

Dr Barker was a keen plantsman and he selected many good forms of plants for his large garden. In dappled shade he planted *Cornus nuttallii*, the Pacific dogwood, a small tree from the west of America, where it varies in size from a shrub to a tree of 50 ft (15 m) or more. When originally discovered in 1826, by David Douglas, it was thought to be a form of the eastern *Cornus florida*. However, Thomas Nuttall, a Yorkshireman who had emigrated to North America, rediscovered the plant about 1836 and realized that it was a distinct species. The flowers of *Cornus nuttallii* are arranged in a small central spherical head surrounded commonly by six large petal-like bracts 1½–3 in. (4–7.5 cm) long, yellowish-white when opening in May, and later becoming pink-toned with age; whereas *C. florida* has usually only four bracts. Nuttall sent information about the tree to his friend, John James Audubon, who painted the famous book *The Birds of America*, also mentioning that pigeons and band-tailed doves fed on the berries; Audubon named the plant after his friend. (PLATE 21)

The plant is probably the most attractive of the dogwood species. One of the many distinguished visitors to Casa di Sole was Harold Hillier who, on seeing Dr Barker's plant of *Cornus nuttallii*, said that it was the best form he had seen. Material was then obtained by the late Lionel Fortescue at The Garden House, Buckland Monachorum, and distributed as *Cornus nuttallii* 'Portlemouth'.

CRINODENDRON HOOKERIANUM
Lantern tree

Among the many treasures introduced by William Lobb on his second trip to South America (1845–8), was the striking and beautiful Lantern Tree that we know today as *Crinodendron hookerianum*. The nomenclature is very confusing but the eighth edition of Bean says: "It is better known in gardens as *Tricuspidaria lanceolata*, but the generic name *Crinodendron* has priority." To confuse the issue further, Lobb originally introduced the plant as *Tricuspidaria dependens*, which is, in fact, a synonym of *C. patagua*, the white-flowered species.

It makes a dense, somewhat erect evergreen shrub, up to 20 ft (6.5 m) or more, with the shoots covered in lanceolate leaves. The flower buds are produced in the autumn and develop through the winter months to open into 1 in. (2.5 cm) long carmine red lanterns on the ends of similarly coloured 2 in. (5 cm) long slender stalks in May. The plant is a forest shrub of the Andes and tolerates light shade. It prefers a humus-rich, lime-free, fertile, moist soil in which it will grow fast. It is unfortunately a shrub only for the milder climates of the South West and for sheltered gardens. In a severe winter the leaf margins may suffer from scorching, but the plant is seldom killed once established. As it has the power of sprouting from old wood, it can be cut back very hard if it becomes too tall or misshapen.

The plant is easily propagated by half-mature cuttings 2½–3½ in. (6–9 cm) long, with a heel. When taken during July and August and placed in a sun frame or mist unit these will root within twenty-eight days, but potting should not be carried out until the following spring. Seed is not readily available and the germination of seeds stratified in a cold frame is usually slow, erratic and poor.

Towards the end of his life William Lobb had more or less settled in California, where he suffered paralysis of the legs and died in San Francisco in May 1864. His brother Thomas, who also collected for Veitch, died at his home at Devoran, between Falmouth and Truro. He is buried in the churchyard there and around a memorial plaque grow some of his introductions, amongst which is William's lovely *Crinodendron*. (PLATE 22)

DAPHNE ODORA 'Baker's Gold'

Over a period of some eighteen years, Ambrose and Patricia Baker of Keeper's Cottage, Dean Prior, have turned an old orchard, with a stream on the boundary, into a garden full of plant treasures. In 1988, these two dedicated gardeners received the RHS Award of Merit for a sport which appeared on their plant of *Daphne odora* 'Aureomarginata'.

Daphnes are not plants renowned for their good nature. Indeed they could even be called treacherous. Almost all daphnes are very sweet on the surface, their blossoms emitting an evocative scent, while lurking in the tissues are poisons strong enough to cause death in children and domestic or farm animals. Even the name Daphne is misleading. The nymph Daphne was in fact transformed into a Bay Tree (*Laurus nobilis*) in order to escape from the attentions of Apollo. The similarity of some daphne plants to the bay may have caused the confusion and encouraged the names 'Dwarf Bay', 'Laureola', and 'Daphne'.

Daphnes are also extremely temperamental, possessing the habit of dying suddenly when apparently healthy and vigorous. One of the least temperamental is *Daphne odora*, introduced in 1771 from Japan. This evergreen shrub can reach nearly 6 ft (2 m), but is usually much lower and likes a well-drained loam. The commonly grown cultivar is 'Aureomarginata' which has leaves edged with a thin line of gold, and is hardier than the non-variegated form. A dense canopy of foliage can make it a useful ground-cover plant, thereby discouraging soil cultivation around its roots, which may be the reason why this plant does not die so readily as many others.

A plant of this cultivar, growing in a bed on the north-west side of the Bakers' cottage, produced a sport with considerably more gold on its leaves, making a plant with a striking gold variegation far superior to its parent. A gale broke away most of the original plant and the new form has grown into a shrub 3 ft (1 m) high and nearly 4½ ft (1.5 m) across. It is hardy, was unaffected by the vicious winters of 1985–7 and gives a bright splash of gold all year round, even on the dullest day. Like its parent, the flowers are very fragrant, ½ in. (12 mm) across, very pale pink inside, but streaked outside dark, purplish red.

Propagation is difficult by cuttings, so stocks are being increased by grafting. When widely available it should supersede its parent, to which it is vastly superior.

(PLATE 23)

PLATE 12
Camellia williamsii 'Mildred Veitch'
at St Bridget Nursery, Exeter

PLATE 13
Camellia 'Carolyn Snowden'
at Marwood Hill, near Barnstaple

PLATE 14
Cantua buxifolia
at Forde Abbey, Dorset

PLATE 15
Ceanothus × veitchianus
at Cannington College, Somerset

PLATE 16
Ceanothus papillosus
at Cannington College, Somerset

PLATE 17
Cistus 'Anne Palmer'
at Chelsea Physic Garden

J. Lloyd

PLATE 18
Clematis 'Mary Rose'
at Peveril Nursery, Christow

B. Fretwell

PLATE 19
Clematis 'The Princess of Wales'
at Peveril Nursery, Christow

J. Lloyd

PLATE 20
Clematis 'John Huxtable'
at Peveril Nursery

A. Baker

PLATE 21
Cornus nuttallii 'Portlemouth'
at The Garden House, Buckland Monachorum

R. Fulcher

PLATE 22
Crinodendron hookerianum
at Inverewe Gardens, Wester Ross

M. Feesey

PLATE 23
Daphne odora 'Baker's Gold'
at Keeper's Cottage, Deancombe

DENDROMECON RIGIDA
Tree poppy

This beautiful shrub was introduced by William Lobb about 1854, while he was collecting for Messrs Veitch. It gained the RHS Award of Merit in 1913.

A native of California, it had been discovered earlier by David Douglas, growing on dry slopes and stony wastes in the chaparral and foothills, and its natural habitat is an indication of the growing conditions which suit it best in the garden. The plant should thrive in a sheltered, sunny position in a well-drained loam to which mortar rubble has been added. It is, however, tender and usually needs protection over the coldest winter months.

The bright yellow, poppy-like blooms, some 2–3 in. (5–7.5 cm) across, are fragrant and borne singly above blue-green narrow leaves in the months from April to June. A bush can reach as high as 10 ft (3 m) but, as a general rule, is much shorter.

Nodal cuttings, taken during July and August, and placed in a close frame or mist, root unreliably. Greater success can be obtained from pencil-thick root cuttings, taken from established plants during December, and placed singly and horizontally in small pots of loam-based seed compost. The pots should be kept in a warm frame until the cuttings are well established. When propagating by this method, roots should be taken from the parent with great care by digging a small trench 12 in. (30 cm) away from the base. The soil should then be washed away from the roots before removing any cuttings. Afterwards, the trench should be filled with good fresh soil, firmed down well and finally watered.   (PLATE 24)

DESFONTAINEA SPINOSA

At first glance, the untutored eye could well be deceived into thinking that *Desfontainea spinosa* was a type of holly. William Lobb, however, would quickly have recognized the masquerade when he found the small 10 ft (3 m) evergreen shrub, with its oval spiny leaves, in the cool Andean mountain rain forests of Chile.

The leaves, while looking very much like a holly, are held opposite to each other and not spirally, as in all *Ilex* species. The plant bears waxy, 1½ in. (4 cm) long, crimson, funnel-shaped blooms, each ending in five yellow shallow lobes. It is hardy only in sheltered districts, particularly in the moister west where a happy plant can look spectacular from July right through to early autumn.

In the wild, *Desfontainea spinosa* ranges from the cool cloud forests of the Colombian Andes south to the sea shores of Tierra del Fuego, and on to the chain of islands along the south Chilean coast. Small wonder then that various leaf shapes and flower colour forms have been reported. In recent years a striking variegated leaf form has been available.

Seed is a ready means of propagation but, unfortunately, many seedlings are inferior, with smaller flowers, sparsely produced. Late autumn cuttings of short sideshoots in a protected cold frame give a good rooting percentage; so too do half-mature cuttings taken in July and raised under polythene or mist.

It is perhaps interesting that this plant was until quite recently classed by botanists in the same family as *Buddleja*; now they are separate.   (PLATE 25)

DIANTHUS

Not since the days of Montague Allwood has any grower made a greater contribution to the development and popularity of Pinks than the late Cecil Wyatt of Bovey Tracey.

Beloved by cottage gardeners of the past and still a favourite today, the 'Divine Flower' or *Dianthus*, took its name from *Dias* (God or divine) and *Anthus* (flower). In the language of flowers, *Dianthus* has many other meanings, depending on the colour of its flowers. It has been called 'Woman's Love', 'Always Lovely', 'Aversion', 'Pure Ardent Love', 'Fascinating' and 'Ingeniousness' or 'Talent'.

Dianthus has been a traditional Devon crop for many years and Cecil's lifelong interest in pinks and carnations was rekindled when he and his family moved to Devon where he met local growers and, in particular, Reg Farley, who kept a nursery at Dawlish where cut flowers were grown in the open. At that time, all such crops were prone to attack by injurious fungi. With the help of Geoff Griffin, a plant pathologist at the Ministry of Agriculture establishment at Starcross, stocks of pinks were selected and propagated which were free from these diseases. As a result of this work and high standards of husbandry, aided by the Nuclear Stock Association Ltd, today's Dawlish nurserymen, like John Whetman, can grow crops in the open and under glass or polythene, which are free from such fungal diseases and all the carnation viruses.

It is, however, for the galaxy of varieties which he raised that Cecil Wyatt will, perhaps, be best remembered. He had an instinctive 'feel' for the progeny that different crosses would produce, rather than any scientific programme, and he achieved a remarkably high rate of success. The flowers he raised had their origins in the hybrid pinks produced by Montague Allwood from 1910–60. Two of Allwood's early hybrids, in particular, 'Doris' and 'Joy' are still very popular and have been the base for many breeding programmes.

Cecil Wyatt started a breeding programme using mixed pollen, in later years on his own varieties. The method he used was to transfer the pollen, using a finger or thumb, instead of tweezers or the traditional camel-hair brush. His superb white 'Haytor' was quickly taken up by the industry and was soon followed by many more, some of which gained the highest awards. He died in March 1986, but his stock, seedlings and seeds from earlier hybridizing were passed to fellow growers who, with Cecil, have been responsible for the increasing popularity of pinks as a long-lasting cut flower. It is expected that many new, worthwhile varieties will result after the seedlings have been screened. John Whetman has also selected such varieties as 'Houndspool Cheryl', 'Devon Cream' and 'Houndspool Ruby'. Another grower in the Devon Pinks Nursery Group, Ray Hubbard, of Hill House Nursery, Landscove, near Ashburton, has hybridized and selected numerous varieties, notably 'Buckfast Abbey' and 'Old Mother Hubbard'. AM 1988. (PLATES 26–30)

The Devon pinks which appear, with descriptions, in the plant list at the back of the book can only partly cover the ever-increasing range; they have names to conjure with and stand as a testimony to the skill of those who raised them.

DICENTRA FORMOSA 'Langtrees'

Dicentra formosa is among the most graceful of herbaceous plants. A native of moist woods from California to British Columbia, it was brought to Britain as long ago as 1796.

In late spring to early summer the arching sprays of drooping, tubular, locket-shaped flowers rise above ferny hummocks of beautifully divided leaves. Each flower has two spurs which give the genus its name: *dis* in Greek meaning two, and *kentron*, spurs; it is undeniably beautiful – and so *formosa*.

Dicentra formosa 'Langtrees' was a distinct form selected by Dr Rogerson in his garden Langtrees at Croyde in north Devon. The flowers, in May, are of palest pink with grey-green foliage. It is thought that *D. oregona*, which has similarly coloured leaves, may well be another parent or grandparent of *D.f.* 'Langtrees', as well as of other readily obtainable varieties such as 'Adrian Bloom' (carmine-crimson) and 'Alba' (white).

The plant prefers cool sites in the garden and does well at the base of small trees where the canopy is not sufficiently dense to dry out the soil. Propagation is best carried out in early spring as growth commences. Division should be done with great care to avoid damaging the fleshy roots.   (PLATE 31)

EMBOTHRIUM COCCINEUM
Chilean fire bush

The distribution of *Embothrium* and other plants in both South America and Australia reflects these continents' common origin in the great land mass of Gondwanaland that finally broke up about 65 million years ago. Gardeners will know the most popular species, *E. coccineum*, as the Chilean fire bush. A plant introduced by William Lobb for Veitch of Exeter in 1846, it created a sensation when first exhibited in bloom, and was given an Award of Merit in 1928; historians probably think of the plant as one that was named from a specimen collected earlier during Captain Cook's second voyage of discovery. Richard Pearce collected a slightly different coloured form between 1860 and 1862. The majority of plants grown today are based on the 'Norquinco Valley form' (AM 1932 and FCC 1948), collected by H.F. Comber in 1925, which are partly deciduous and usually hardier than the evergreens.

The Chilean fire bush in full bloom, from May to July, is an unforgettable sight with the brilliant crimson- or orange-scarlet flowers crowded in dense cylindrical racemes 3½–5in. (9–12 cm) long, reminiscent of a honeysuckle.

The plant needs a moisture-retentive but well-drained loam, preferably with added peat; it is not tolerant of any lime in the soil. Propagation is by seed in the winter sown under glass in seed compost low in phosphate (careful watching is needed as they are very susceptible to damping off) or by 1¼ in. (3 cm) long root cuttings, again under heated glass, or rooted suckers lifted carefully from established plants.   (PLATE 32)

ERICA ARBOREA 'Picos Pigmy'
Tree heath

Erica arborea 'Picos Pigmy' was found by Terry Underhill in 1973 in the rugged Picos Mountains of northern Spain and posted home to Devon by airmail in a silver paper tube.

In contrast to 'Picos Pigmy', the taller *Erica arborea* (the tree heath) can make a small tree or large bush 20 ft (7 m) tall, and is native to the warm climates of the Mediterranean and the higher mountains of East and Central Africa. In Europe it often grows on poor and sandy, alkaline (limy) soils, usually on the edge of oak and olive woods. It is tender and could be killed by a cold British winter, although it will stand some twelve degrees of frost for one or two nights. The large roots of this shrub are sometimes boiled, turned and polished to produce 'briar' pipes, so beloved of smokers world-wide.

At 4200 ft (1300 m) above sea level, the variety 'Alpina' has learned to keep its head well down and achieves only about one-third of the height of *Erica arborea*, of which it is a much tougher dwarf form, although it, too, can suffer during a cold winter.

The slopes of the Picos are covered with the dwarf forms of this very sweetly scented shrub. From a stand on a very exposed ridge, Terry Underhill selected a particular dwarf form which was bushy, highly scented, very floriferous, with large, pure white flowers. Appropriately for its size it was named 'Picos Pigmy'. The original cuttings, some fifteen years later, have reached a maximum of 5½ ft (1.75 m). During late April and May the plants, still with their old foliage of olive to dark green, are clothed with flowers that attract bees from far and wide. After flowering, fresh growth is a pleasing apple green. The parents grow on a site which is neither particularly exposed nor sheltered and they survived the winters of 1985–6 and 1986–7 unscathed.   (PLATE 33)

ERYSIMUM 'L.K. Elmhirst'

In the early 1930s there was a great deal of nationwide discussion about the rural revitalization taking place around the ruins of Dartington Hall and its garden. Arguments raged about the attitude there towards co-education, music, drama and other arts, forestry and agricultural research as well as gardening; not to mention the fact that Dartington was employing 600 local people at national rates of pay instead of the depressed rates of most other employers in the South West. The whole concept had been envisaged by Leonard Elmhirst, a Yorkshire-man, and his wife, Dorothy Witney Straight, the Americans' 'special lady'.

As they rebuilt the Hall and its farm buildings they developed a team of knowledgeable managers. Dorothy had, among many talents, an outstanding feel for colour and design and, with the help of Beatrix Farrand from America, R.S. Lynch from Cambridge and of Kew Botanical Gardens, she set about rebuilding the Hall gardens. At the same time Mr Lynch set up specialized nurseries on the estate. Symons Tree Nursery became the most up-to-date tree and shrub propagation unit in the world, while Lanes End, at the bottom of the Dartington Drive at Totnes, developed alpines, dwarf shrubs and conifers. A limited amount of hybridizing took place as well as plant selection. They developed techniques of building large, natural-looking rock gardens to order, as part of an expanding landscape service. Their combined efforts won many successive Gold Medals at the Chelsea Flower Show.

During these earlier years many new and exciting plants were sold, and the Dartington catalogues of this era contain a number of plants sadly now lost to cultivation; many catalogue plants were illustrated by wood-cut prints. Among the plants listed, without any notes as to parentage, is *Erysimum* 'L.K. Elmhirst'. It is a robust wallflower, quickly making a 1½–2 ft (45–60 cm) dome of narrow grey-green leaves above which are clusters of lavender purple flowers. When planted in a well-drained loam, in a sunny position, it will often flower continuously. One plant, in the Dartington Hall gardens, flowered non-stop for over twelve years (1964–77), which must be something of a record. It surely did not deserve its untimely end when workers on the roof of a nearby building covered it in molten bitumen! *Erysimum* 'L.K. Elmhirst' did not have such a strong colour as 'Bowles Mauve', or such a thick, large-leaved, robust appearance. Various names have appeared in catalogues, such as *E.* 'Dorothy Elmhirst', 'Dorothy' and 'Mrs L.K. Elmhirst', which are possibly varieties of this plant. (PLATE 34)

ERYTHRONIUM REVOLUTUM 'Knightshayes Pink'
Trout lily

The European dog's-tooth violet – *Erythronium dens-canis* – makes marvellous displays in the grassy meadows of mountainous areas, thriving whether in sun or shade, with or without lime. The North American *Erythronium* spp., however, prefer semi-shade in moister soils that must never dry out during their growing season.

Probably the most beautiful and easiest to cultivate is *E. revolutum*, found in damp coastal woodlands, and at the edges of bogs, swamps and rivers, from northern California to southern British Columbia. Because of its marbled leaves it is commonly known as the Trout lily. The large flowers, one to three on a

PLATE 24
Dendromecon rigida,
at Forde Abbey, Dorset

J. Lloyd

PLATE 25
Desfontainea spinosa
at Inverewe Gardens, Wester Ross

R. Fulcher

PLATE 26
Dianthus 'Old Mother Hubbard'
at Hill House, Landscove

A. Baker

PLATE 28
Dianthus 'Dartmoor Forest'
Original painting by Rosanne Sanders

PLATE 27
Dianthus 'Cranmere Pool'
Original painting by Rosanne Sanders

PLATE 29
Dianthus 'Valda Wyatt'
Original painting by Rosanne Sanders

PLATE 30
Dianthus 'Buckfast Abbey'
at Hill House, Landscove

PLATE 31
Dicentra formosa 'Langtrees'
at The Garden House, Buckland Monachorum

PLATE 32
Embothrium coccineum
at Inverewe Gardens, Wester Ross

PLATE 33
Erica arborea 'Picos Pigmy'
at Fairlight, Rattery

PLATE 34
Erysimum 'L. K. Elmhirst'
at Dartington Hall, near Totnes

PLATE 35
Erythronium revolutum 'Knightshayes Pink'
at Knightshayes, Tiverton

stem, are strongly recurved with broad petals and stand up well above the foliage on 5–6 in. (12–15 cm) stems.

An outstanding form, with much deeper pink flowers than the type, was selected from a batch of seedlings at Knightshayes, Tiverton – the home of so many distinguished plants. *E. revolutum* 'Knightshayes Pink' has up to five deep pink blooms, with dark, mottled leaves, each stem as long as 12 in. (30 cm). Like all *Erythronium* spp., this variety is divided and replanted in organically rich soil after flowering when the leaves die down.   (PLATE 35)

ESCALLONIA

Escallonia macrantha hedges are a common sight in gardens in the South West where they make both formal or informal hedges and screens that withstand coastal conditions, including the salt-laden gales to which the peninsula is prone. It is equally fitting that this genus should be so popular in the South West as it was the Cornishman William Lobb, from Egloshayle, by Wadebridge, who collected the plant on the island of Chiloé and introduced it to Veitch's nursery at Exeter in 1848.

It is a densely leafy, strong-growing, roundish bush with its evergreen, oval, shiny leaves, which are aromatic and set off splendidly the panicles of rosy-crimson, tubular flowers. Normal flowering time is during the summer, but often flowers are produced at any time of the year. It is well named *macrantha*, which means large flowered.

Lobb also collected and introduced some other escallonias, such as *E. laevis* from Brazil in 1844, which is a small shrub with shiny aromatic leaves and rosy-red flowers. *E. rosea* came from Patagonia, in Argentina, in 1847. It is a medium-sized evergreen shrub, 6–8 ft (2–2.5 m), but for some peculiar reason it is named *rosea*, which means pink, when, in fact, the flowers are a pure white and fragrant.

Messrs Veitch crossed *E. rosea* and *E. rubra* (of which some botanists believe *macrantha* is a variety) and raised a superb hybrid, named *E.* × 'Exoniensis' which reaches 15–20 ft (4.5–6 m), is vigorous, evergreen, has glossy leaves and white flowers with a blush of pink. It was awarded an AM by the RHS in 1891.

There are over fifty species of the Chilean gum box – as it is popularly called – in South America. They are concentrated particularly in the Andes and were named after a little-known Spanish traveller, Antonio José Escallon y Flores. (PLATES 40-42)

EUCRYPHIA GLUTINOSA

This tree is a joy to behold in July and August, when covered in large, pure white blossoms, each with a conspicuous central boss of golden stamens. It is mainly deciduous and in most autumns the leaves colour to orange and red before falling, making this the most interesting and colourful of the genus.

Richard Pearce rediscovered *Eucryphia glutinosa* in Chile in 1859, whilst collecting for Veitch of Exeter. It had been found some years earlier, out of flower, and was mistaken for a new species of Southern Beech, with paired leaflets, and described under the name of *Fagus glutinosa*. A few years later, about 1845, Gay, a Chilean botanist, found plants in flower and named them *Eucryphia pinnatifolia*.

Eucryphia glutinosa is a very desirable large shrub to grow in all but the smaller gardens, but unfortunately it is not readily available from nurseries, as propagation is not easy. Cuttings will root if caught at the right time in early or mid summer. Seeds can be obtained from healthy mature specimens: just remember that the fruits take over twelve months to ripen and are usually ready for collection by November/December the following year. Good quality seed will germinate if sown in January/February and kept moist in the cold frame or greenhouse. (PLATE 43)

EUPHORBIA CHARACIAS 'Benger's Silver'

'Benger's Silver' is the name given to a chance seedling of the well-known Western Mediterranean winter-foliage plant, which appeared in the paving at Mrs Judy Benger's Burrow Farm garden, near Axminster. The mature leaves are the typical grey-green, but have a silver margin. Young growths are lime green with gold margins, and mature stems a maroon pink. The bracts are cream with a grey-green stripe. The green flowers open during February to April. E.A. Bowles once described the flowers as "curious dull green heads of flowers with their conspicuous black spots ... and I like to call it a name I learnt (in Dublin), the Frog Spawn Bush". This new clone is a very exciting plant which will soon be coming on to the market.
(PLATE 44)

FERNS IN DEVON
by Kenneth Adlam

In the past, the county of Devon has been a happy hunting ground for ferns and many varieties were found, especially during the latter part of the nineteenth century and the early twentieth century. Most of the fern plant hunters were amateur enthusiasts who carefully cultivated their finds, propagating progeny for garden cultivation. Unfortunately, a number of interesting finds have been lost over the years, but many still exist in cultivation.

From among the many well-known Devon fern hunters and growers of the past, we list here but a few, together with some of their outstanding discoveries:

John Dadds of Ilfracombe raised *Dryopteris filix-mas* 'Polydactyla Dadds', a graceful form of the Male Fern, the frond apex being finely tasselled. This fern is still grown and sometimes available from nurseries specializing in ferns. Another attractive fern found in the Ilfracombe district by Dadds was *Dryopteris dilatata* 'Hymenophylloides', a dwarf congested form of the common Broad Buckler Fern, found in many Devon woods. Dadds died in 1904.

Colonel A.M. Jones raised a number of beautiful ferns discovered in Devon, one being the Crested Hay-Scented Buckler Fern, *Dryopteris aemula* 'Cristata'. Jones was also instrumental in cultivating and naming *Athyrium filix-femina* 'Clarissima Jones'. Colonel Jones died in 1889.

Miss Fanny Kitson of Torquay, a clergyman's daughter, was an early admirer and grower of ferns and a hunter of varieties in the wild. One of the ferns found by Fanny Kitson near Torquay was *Polystichum setiferum* 'Kitsonae'; this variety is a form of the Soft Shield Fern, often found in some Devon woods and banks, but unfortunately 'Kitsonae' is now rarely seen.

Robert Moule, from Ilfracombe, was another early hunter who found *Athyrium filix-femina* 'Clarissima Jones' in a north Devon wood. The pinnae of this beautiful but rare fern are very finely divided. In lighter vein, it was compared to a beautiful lady in an article in *The British Fern Gazette* (1915) entitled "The Romance of Lady Clarissima". In fact the fern had been named in memory of his beloved wife by Colonel Jones, who had grown on Moule's find in 1868. Another fern Moule found in Devon was an incised form of the Maidenhair Spleenwort, *Asplenium trichomanes* 'Moulei', still in cultivation but not common.

The Reverend Charles Padley, another Devon fern hunter and a first-rate judge of ferns, found many forms of the Soft Shield Fern, *Polystichum setiferum*,

PLATE 36
Athyrium filix-femina 'Clarissima Jones'

PLATE 37
Athyrium filix-femina 'Clarissima Jones'

including 'Tripinnatum'. Some of his *Polystichum* forms are still about, but difficult to obtain. Padley found at Exmouth a Hard Fern form, *Blechnum spicant* 'Padleyense'.

The Reverend F. Mules found *Blechnum spicant* 'Biceps' near Marwood, north Devon. This Hard Fern has very long-toothed pinnae and fronds forked at the tips.

PLATE 38
Asplenium trichomanes incisum 'Moule'

PLATE 39
Fragaria vesca var. *'fructu hispida'* at Plymouth

FRAGARIA VESCA var. *FRUCTU HISPIDA*
Plymouth strawberry

"A Botanical Dodo" were the words used by Dr Hogg to sum up the Plymouth strawberry. That great plantsman, E.A. Bowles, found it "wrong in the head if ever a plant was" and, accordingly, grew it in a part of his garden known as "The Lunatic Asylum". More charitably perhaps, Bowles conceded it to be "one of the strangest of plants with a wonderfully curious history".

To find out what he meant, we must go back to the mid 1620s when a lady collected roots believing them to be those of the common wild strawberry. She planted them in her mother's Plymouth garden, which is thought to have been a short distance from Sutton harbour. As the fruit was not up to her expectations, she was intending to throw the plants away; fortunately, in November 1627 John Tradescant arrived in Plymouth. He was, at that time, in the service of George Villiers, Duke of Buckingham, and accompanied him on all his military and civil expeditions. The unfortunate Buckingham had put in to Plymouth after the disastrous voyage to the Île de Ré, and the failure of his mission to take La Rochelle. His master's troubles did nothing to dampen Tradescant's passion for collecting rarities, and he removed the Plymouth lady's unwanted plants to his own garden at Lambeth in London and listed them in his catalogue of 1634 as *Fragaria spinosa* sive *hispida*.

The earliest reference to the Plymouth strawberry is by a friend of John Tradescant, John Parkinson, who wrote in his *Paradisus* of 1629:

One Strawberry more I promised to shew you, which, though it be a wilde kinde, and of no use for meate, yet I would not let this discourse passe with out giving you the knowledge of it. It is in leafe much like unto the ordinary, but differeth in that the flower, if it have any, is greene, or rather it beareth a small head of greene leaves, many set thicke together like a double ruffe, in the midst whereof standeth the fruit, which when it is ripe, sheweth to be soft and some-what reddish, like unto a Strawberry, but with many small harmless prickles on them, which may be eaten and chewed in the mouth without any maner of offence, and is somewhat pleasant like a Strawberry; it is no great bearer but those it doth beare, are set at the toppes of the stalks close together, pleasant to behold, and fit for a gentlewoman to weare on her arme etc. as a raritie instead of a flower.

Over the next century references were made periodically to this plant. It was then apparently lost, although described in detail by Briggs in *The Flora of*

Plymouth in 1880, who then called it a "monstrosity" of the Common Wild Strawberry. He mentioned that it had not been seen for 150 years. Around that time, in his *Vegetable Teratology*, Dr Masters refers to Dr Hogg's "Botanical Dodo". Shortly after publication of this work, Dr Masters rediscovered the Plymouth strawberry growing in Canon Ellacombe's famous garden at Bitton, near Bristol. He obtained some plants and, in the best traditions of gardeners, passed some on to Mr Bowles.

Though still uncommon, the plant has since been somewhat more widely distributed. It is hardy and will grow in any reasonable soil, a few inches high, running, and flowers with Elizabethan-type green ruffs during May and June. In his book *My Garden in Spring*, E.A. Bowles described the blossoms as having every part "changed into leafy structures; the petals are little green leaves, even the anthers and carpels are replaced by tufts of tubular leaves". Of the fruit, he says it has "red flesh studded with the tubular leaves instead of pips, and with two ranks of leaflets round the base".

With the Plymouth or 'Prickly' strawberry safely back in cultivation once again, we are left to ponder on the possible fate of this plant if Buckingham had been successful at the siege of La Rochelle.   (PLATE 39)

FUCHSIA

In the early part of the nineteenth century many fuchsias found their way into this country, several collected by William Lobb for Veitch. They immediately became popular as greenhouse plants and were hybridized extensively. One of the most important breeders was William Storey of White Hill, Newton Abbot, who had the distinction of introducing the first double fuchsia, the first striped one, and the first with a white corolla. The list of his, and other breeders' work, is included in the *Hortus Devoniensis* at the end of the book.   (PLATES 45-47)

Messrs Lucombe & Pince raised, in 1842, the hybrid *Fuchsia* 'Exoniensis' (*splendens* × 'Globosa'). They then crossed the climbing *F. regia* with 'Exoniensis' to produce the better-known 'Corallina'. This was a strongly growing, lax, hardy shrub with red and purple flowers, and it became an important parent. (The fuchsia under this name today, though otherwise similar, is sterile.)

John Dominy of Veitch raised a hybrid between *F. splendens* and *F. magellanica* in 1852, named 'Dominiana' – a tender, autumn-flowering shrub with red flowers. It was popular in Victorian winter gardens and received an Award of Merit in 1853.

More recently, George Hilton of Plymouth produced a number of cultivars which are popular today. Among these are the splendidly named 'Devonshire Dumpling' and 'Drake Fourhundred'.

Chris Brickell, Director of the RHS, noticed a variegated shoot growing on *Fuchsia magellanica* at Overbecks, the National Trust house and garden just outside Salcombe. The plant was propagated and named 'Sharpitor'. It has pale pink flowers and the leaves are variegated, with a pale cream margin.

The long growing season, created by the relatively mild climate of much of Devon, is well suited to the growing of fuchsias. In a sheltered spot, given a mild winter, many greenhouse varieties will survive outdoors without protection and the hardy types will retain most of their leaves and flower continuously.

HOYA

Thomas Lobb introduced a number of species of *Hoya* from Java and Malaya, but *Hoya bella* he found on the Talung Kola Mountain, Moulmein, Burma. First exhibited in June 1848 by Veitch of Exeter, its description in the *Botanical Magazine* waxes lyrical – "the most lovely of all the hoyas, resembling an amethyst set in silver". Its popular name is the miniature wax plant, and the flowers, borne in flat clusters, are waxy-white with a purple or rose-crimson corona, and very strongly scented. The leaves are fleshy, and the habit drooping, making it an excellent subject for hanging baskets. It requires a warm greenhouse with semi-shade.

Another species pictured here is *H. cinnamomifolia* which Veitch flowered for the first time in July 1847. It has pale, yellow-green flowers, with a deep purple-red corona. The leaves are large, 8 in. (20 cm) long, oval with long narrow points, similar to those of cinnamon. It climbs to about 10 ft (4 m).

The genus is named after Thomas Hoy, a former Head Gardener at Syon House.   (PLATES 48, 49)

HYACINTHOIDES HISPANICA 'Chevithorne'
Spanish bluebell

Chevithorne Barton, near Tiverton, is a garden where many plants have been skilfully encouraged to naturalize and fit into the landscape, irrespective of their country of origin. The Spanish Bluebell, from the Iberian Peninsula and North

C. Rogers

PLATE 40
Escallonia rubra macrantha at Kiln House, Brixham

E. Pickard

PLATE 41
Escallonia × 'Exoniensis'
at Rumleigh Experimental Station, Bere Alston

E. Pickard

PLATE 42
Escallonia laevis
at Rumleigh Experimental Station

M. Russell

PLATE 43
Eucryphia glutinosa
at Crediton

M. Squires

PLATE 44
Euphorbia characias 'Benger's Silver'
at Burrow Farm Garden, Dalwood

R. Fulcher

PLATE 45
Fuchsia 'Corallina'
at Bicton College, East Budleigh

PLATE 46
Fuchsia 'Devonshire Dumpling'
at Hill House, Landscove

PLATE 47
Fuchsia 'Drake Fourhundred'
at Elburton, Plymouth

PLATE 48
Hoya bella at Little Southey, Northcott

PLATE 49
Hoya cinnamomifolia

PLATE 50
Hyacinthoides hispanica 'Chevithorne'
at Knightshayes, Tiverton

PLATE 51
Iris unguicularis 'Mary Barnard'
at Keeper's Cottage, Deancombe

Africa, has certainly made itself at home and large drifts enjoy the dappled shade from a light woodland canopy, in the same way as does our native Bluebell. Unlike our familiar plant which bears its flowers on one side of the stem, its Spanish cousin is distinguished by its ascending conical clusters of violet-blue bell-shaped blooms, each with blue anthers, borne on tall, robust stems.

The variety 'Chevithorne' is deep blue, slightly scented and larger and more vigorous in all respects than the type. In 1956 it received an Award of Merit from the RHS. There is a possibility that the original stock from which 'Chevithorne' arose came from an Irish garden.

This species is a nomenclature nightmare having been given, at various times, the generic names of *Scilla*, *Hyacinthus*, *Agraphis*, *Endymion* and now *Hyacinthoides*. Whilst accepting that there have been good reasons for the changes, let us hope that for the sake of this easily grown, attractive plant it is soon given a name to match its good nature! (PLATE 50)

IRIS UNGUICULARIS 'Mary Barnard'
Algerian iris

The late Mary Barnard, after whom this outstanding iris was named, was a keen gardener from Honiton who, somewhat adventurously for the late 1930s, decided to holiday in Algiers. Whilst there, she came upon, and brought back to Devon, a rich intense violet, floriferous and strongly scented form of *Iris unguicularis*.

Such was her generosity that, on her return, she gave some to her friend John Grey (of snowdrop fame) at Saxmundham. He, in turn, gave a plant to E.B. Anderson, who was at that time gardening at Porlock in Somerset. Anderson was so very impressed with this iris because of its colour and scented blooms – not to mention its habit, when happy, of flowering freely every year when others failed, and its ability to set seed annually – that he named the clone 'Mary Barnard'. He registered it in 1962, along with a large pale lavender clone named 'Walter Butt'. E.B. Anderson grew several plants from seed which resulted in a darker tone, and these he marketed as 'Mary Barnard Improved'.

Iris unguicularis was first described by Poiret in 1789 in his *Voyage en Barbarie* and his name for this delightful winter-flowering plant must stand by the law of priority, as Desfontaines' name, *I. stylosa*, was not published until 1798 in his *Flora Atlantica*. "Unguicularis" means "having a claw(s)" and refers to the shape at the base of the petals. The typical plant from Algeria forms a dense grassy tuft of sword-like leaves up to 2 ft (60 cm) high, among which, during the winter months, nestle pale violet flowers, beautifully marked and veined with cream and yellow. However, it is very variable and several deeper violet forms have been described and collected. One such was the plant brought back by Mrs Mary Barnard.

Being Mediterranean plants, all forms of *Iris unguicularis* require a hot summer and not too cold a winter to give of their best. In Britain a position at the foot of a south-facing wall in poor limy soil with the addition of some builder's rubble would be ideal. Rhizomes should be planted on or near the surface to enable them to become well ripened. In heavy soils a raised bed would be necessary to grow this iris successfully.

The simplest method of propagation is by division in late August, just as the new roots are starting growth; this enables the divisions to establish quickly in the warm soil. This is also the month to go over the clumps with shears and reduce the luxuriant growth by half, thus admitting the sun to help ripen the rhizomes; it is also the time to clear dead leaves which offer shelter to slugs and snails. E.A. Bowles gave us the cultural hints needed to grow and flower this plant, which incidentally is ideal for winter cutting, when he wrote, "Patience seems to be the only manure these irises need, poor soil inducing flowering instead of production of leaf, and the older a clump grows, the better it flowers".

Mary Barnard died in 1947, but her gardening skills were passed on to her son, Richard Barnard, who specialized in Eucalypts, and started the Eucalyptus Grove at Grey Timbers, near Bovey Tracey, in 1956. *Iris unguicularis* 'Mary Barnard' is widely cultivated in our gardens today – a reminder of a generous lady who was only too willing to share her precious find with her fellow gardeners.   (PLATE 51)

KNIPHOFIA 'Mermaiden'
Red-hot poker

At one time the National Collection of *Kniphofias* was grown at Coleton Fishacre in south Devon. Sadly the collection was moved to the Isle of Wight, but many plants of this large genus grow in Devon, enjoying the maritime climate. An enthusiastic couple with an interest in these plants is Mr and Mrs F.J. Holmes from Sidbury. They raised a magnificent hybrid *Kniphofia* 'Mermaiden' in 1979, by crossing 'Prince Igor' with 'Maid of Orleans', which are two fine garden plants. Many seedlings were produced from the cross which were grown on, with the aim of finding a neat plant suitable for the average garden ('Prince Igor' being very tall and vigorous). In the summer of 1981, a plant produced two 7 in. (18 cm) spikes of greeny-cream, and this is now in cultivation. The hybrid is vigorous to a height of 3 ft (90 cm). The flowering spikes all appear at the same time. This is a very gardenworthy addition to the popular race of hardy and half-hardy perennials. (PLATE 52)

LAPAGERIA ROSEA and *L.R. ALBIFLORA*
Chilean bell-flower

Lapageria rosea is the national flower of Chile, where it is called Copihue. Since its introduction and the first flowering of an isolated plant at Kew in 1847, it has, quite rightly, been prized as one of the most beautiful of evergreen glasshouse climbers.

Imagine how thrilled William Lobb must have been when he discovered it trailing among the shrubs and trees in the woods of Chile, where it often climbs to 12–15 ft (4–5 m), its smooth and slender woody shoots twined around the supporting thickets. After all the hardships of his journey he would have been rewarded by the sight of the long pendulous bells of its flowers of some 3 in. (7.5 cm) hanging towards the end of the shoots from the axils of the large dark green leathery leaves. The flowers are made up of thick wax-like fleshy segments, the inner ones of which are rich rosy crimson, faintly spotted with rose. Seed collected by Lobb from the fruit, a 2 in. (5 cm) long, green-yellow berry, was sent home from his 1845–8 expedition to Veitch in Exeter where plants were raised in some quantity.

In 1860, another beautiful variety, *L.r. albiflora*, bearing white flowers touched with a hint of ivory cream, was sent back by Richard Pearce, one of the many men who collected for the Veitches in South America; this first flowered in 1862. Plants were raised by layering, and also from seed, which can not be relied upon to come true to colour.

It should be said that the first plant of this white form to be introduced into Europe was sent to the Jardin des Plantes, Paris, by Monsieur Abadi, where it flowered in 1855. The plant that flowered at Kew in 1847 was a single plant sent by R. Wheelwright. Nevertheless, it was the two collectors Pearce and Lobb, working for Veitch, who introduced the plants in such quantity that they became available to gardeners to grow in their cool glasshouses, where they can cover rafters or north-facing walls. The plants will even grow out of doors in partially shaded spots in protected parts of the South West.

Lapageria was named in honour of the first wife of Napoleon Bonaparte, Empress Josephine (Tascher de la Pagerie), herself a keen plantswoman.
(PLATES 53, 54)

LILIUM
Lily

Lilies, the aristocrats of the bulb world, must surely be some of the most desirable of garden plants, with their dignified growth and beauty of flower. They are, generally, equally adaptable in a herbaceous border, interplanted among rhododendrons and other shrubs, or grown in pots that can be moved at will. Some have a comparatively undemanding nature, while others are notoriously fickle and hard to please. The general 'rule of thumb' is to provide a well-drained but moisture-retentive soil and all the sun they can get (with the exception of the fierce midday sun), provided that their roots are kept cool. High winter rainfall can spell disaster to many of the species, as can the virus disorders that are so readily spread by aphids.

With these problems in mind, at least one Devon lily specialist, Derek Gardham, of Blackdown Lilies, Newton Poppleford, who studied the genus in this country and the USA, is breeding new varieties. Many of these make ideal garden plants, being grown to flowering bulb size in the open fields. Amongst these are the 'Devon Dawn' hybrids, which are virus free. He has also raised the 'Coral Reef' strain of *longiflorum* hybrids. As his breeding programme develops, gardeners will be able to enjoy the colour, form and scent of many lilies year after year without regular replanting or fear of virus and winter rotting.

Mary Lees grew several lilies in her small garden, Staplers at Sticklepath near Okehampton. In the 1960s she was selling her own vigorous strain of *L. × testaceum*, the Nankeen lily, probably the oldest recorded lily hybrid, the parents being *L. candidum × L. chalcedonicum*. In June and July it has up to twelve very large, hanging turkscap flowers, of apricot-yellow, with a few red spots, on 6–7 ft (2 m) stems, which are purple with a greyish bloom. It is still in cultivation; as *L. × testaceum* is prone to mosaic virus, perhaps the Mary Lees strain has some resistance to this crippling disorder.
(PLATES 55–60)

C. Rogers

PLATE 52
Kniphofia 'Mermaiden'
at Coleton Fishacre, Kingswear

J. Primmer

PLATE 53
Lapageria rosea
at Bicton College, East Budleigh

D. Donald

PLATE 54
Lapageria rosea albiflora

A. Baker

PLATE 55
Lilium × *testaceum* Mary Lees strain
at Keeper's Cottage, Deancombe

PLATE 56
Lilium 'Devon Dawn hybrid'
at Blackdown Lilies, Newton Poppleford

PLATE 57
Lilium 'Devon Dawn hybrid'
at Blackdown Lilies

PLATE 58
Lilium 'Devon Dawn hybrid'
at Blackdown Lilies

PLATE 59
Lilium 'Devon Dawn hybrid'
at Blackdown Lilies

PLATE 60
Lilium longiflorum 'Coral Reef strain'
at Blackdown Lilies

PLATE 61
Lomatia ferruginea
at Coleton Fishacre, Kingswear

LOMATIA FERRUGINEA

This magnificent evergreen foliage plant, which is often grown as a multi-stemmed small tree or a large bush, is a native of the rain forests of Chile and Patagonia. It was introduced through William Lobb to Veitch between 1845 and 1848. It has large, much divided, fern-like leaves that are deep green above and a downy white below that turns brown with age, all held on velvety stems. The flowers, produced in July, are in clusters to about 2 in. (5 cm) long and are dull red and buff, and of similar structure to *Embothrium*, with which it is allied. The plant was given an Award of Merit in 1927. Hardy only in the milder parts of the South West it was one of the many exciting plants discovered growing at Coleton Fishacre, near Dartmouth, when the house and garden were given to the National Trust.

It propagates readily from half-mature side shoots, 2–3 in. (5–7.5 cm) long, taken with a trimmed heel. Cuttings should be placed in a gently shaded close frame with bottom heat or in a partly shaded mist unit. They resent root disturbance when young, so they should be rooted individually in small pots. Even when planted outside in a warm sheltered site, they need at least a year to become established, and are happiest in light shade in a lime-free soil, high in humus and low in phosphate, moist but well-drained.   (PLATE 61)

MAGNOLIA

Enough has been written elsewhere about this most splendid genus of flowering trees, almost every species of which is represented in Britain, and which flourishes happily in the softer moist climate of the South West. Four kinds qualify for inclusion in a book on Devon garden plants.   (PLATES 63–68)

Magnolia campbellii 'Sidbury'

Young plants of a cross between *M. campbellii* and *M. mollicomata* were probably made in the 1930s by Sir Charles Cave's gardener, Mr Barton, at Sidbury Manor, Sidbury. The late Sir Harold Hillier's father was given a plant, and from it Messrs Hillier propagated and distributed under the name 'Sidbury'. There are still plants from the original cross in the garden at Sidbury, all slightly different, as splendid as *campbellii* when flowering, which the hybrid does from a younger age.

Magnolia grandiflora 'Exmouth'

The original tree, growing in the Exmouth garden of Sir John Colleton, was noted by Miller in his *Gardener's Dictionary* of 1768 as being one of the few sizeable specimens in the country, most of the first introductions having succumbed to the severe frosts of 1739–40. Therefore layers from the Exmouth tree were much in demand by nurserymen. Sadly, the tree was cut down by accident in 1794.

'Exmouth' forms a narrower tree than the typical Bull Bay, making it less liable to snow damage. The shining deep evergreen leaves are also somewhat narrower. The white flowers, produced in late summer and autumn are up to 10 in. (25 cm) across and have a strong spicy fragrance. It flowers at an earlier age than the type. It is likely that 'Exmouth' has a little *Magnolia virginiana* blood, probably gained in the wild, which should enhance its hardiness. The leaves and flowers are shown on the Exmouth coat of arms, and it was sometimes known as *M. grandiflora* 'Exoniensis'. It won an Award of Garden Merit in 1969.

Magnolia × *veitchii*

Peter Veitch worked at the Veitch nurseries in Chelsea during the first part of his life, spending three years collecting plants with F.W. Burbidge in Australasia and Borneo. In 1880 he was appointed head of the Exeter firm and during this time he raised the magnolia hybrid that bears the family name. In 1907 Peter Veitch crossed *Magnolia campbellii* with *denudata*. Of all the *campbellii* flowers pollinated, only one seed pod resulted. All six seeds in it germinated and within fifteen years all had flowered. Number 3, the first to flower and regarded as the best, was called × *veitchii*. It has fragrant pink flowers with nine petals (tepals) to 6 in. (15 cm) long, and leaves to 12 × 6 in. (30 × 15 cm). It has grown 80 ft (25 m) in forty-six years at Caerhays; the largest growing magnolia in the UK. It was named *M.* × *veitchii* 'Peter Veitch' in 1970, and awarded an FCC in 1921.

The second to flower, Number 6, was not much regarded for many years. It has since been marketed as 'Isca' and has many satiny-white flowers which appear slightly earlier than 'Peter Veitch'. The other seedlings were white blossomed.

Magnolia × *soulangiana* 'Coimbra'

Originally raised by M. Soulange-Bodin near Paris, crossing *M. denudata* with *M. liliflora*, the hybrid first flowered in 1826 and is the magnolia most often seen in English gardens. When Lionel Fortescue, of The Garden House at Buckland

Monachorum, was visiting Portugal, he found a very good clone at the Botanic Gardens there and obtained material which he brought back to Devon and propagated, calling it 'Coimbra'. The flower is large, very pointed, and a rich purple, with paler pink inside. It won the Cory Cup in 1973.

MAHONIA 'Buckland' and 'Lionel Fortescue'

The mahonias have earned a special place in the winter garden for their beautiful evergreen glossy, dark green, pinnate leaves. Many of the species bear spires of sweetly scented flowers, cheering the darkest days. *Mahonia × media* (*japonica × lomariifolia*) has been raised in many places. Two very fine clones were raised in 1971 by Lionel Fortescue, of The Garden House, Buckland Monachorum, with the help of Michael Hickson, who then worked there. 'Buckland' is particularly attractive with 2 ft (60 cm) wide inflorescences, made up of 12–14 branched racemes of pale yellow, fragrant blooms, later than 'Lionel Fortescue', and deservedly was awarded the Cory Cup. 'Lionel Fortescue' differs in having a thicker inflorescence, more erect and with racemes up to 15 in. (40 cm) long. The deep yellow flowers, opening from October through the winter, are again fragrant; this was given, as a seedling, to the Savill Gardens at Windsor, who eventually named it. This mahonia, which gained an Award of Merit in 1975, is one of many which perpetuates the memory of an outstanding plantsman and selector of good garden plants.   (PLATES 69, 70)

MALUS
Apple

When associating apples with Devon, thoughts turn mainly to cider apples and, of course, there are many cider cultivars in the county, but these are outside the scope of this book. Culinary and eating apples are well represented too, and some have long histories. 'Devonshire Quarrendon' was recorded before 1678, of unknown origin, and has small dark crimson-purple fruit, juicy and pleasant to eat.

In the woods at Dean Prior, near Buckfastleigh, Peter Lock found a culinary apple in the early 1800s; a late fruit, greenish-yellow with a few pale red stripes, it was registered with the RHS under the name of its discoverer as 'Peter Lock'.

George Pyne of Denver Nurseries, Topsham, was responsible for many new

Devonshire Quarrendon

Bowden's Seedling

Star of Devon

Woolbrook Russet

Peter Lock

Woolbrook Pippin

PLATE 62
Malus

Original painting by Rosanne Sanders

cultivars of fruit in the early years of this century, and he introduced 'Star of Devon', which was raised by J. Garland of Broadclyst.

F. Bowden of Torquay introduced 'Bowden's Seedling' some time before 1931, very similar to a 'Jonathan' but with a much better flavour. 'Woolbrook Pippin', a seedling of Cox's Orange Pippin, and 'Woolbrook Russet', a good cooking apple with rather acid white flesh, were both raised in 1903 at the Sidmouth nursery of J.H. Stevens. They are among the six (all of which are still in cultivation) chosen, from the large number of apples listed at the end of this book, to be painted from life by Rosanne Sanders, author of *The English Apple*.

MALVA SYLVESTRIS 'Primley Blue'
Common mallow

Herbert Whitley, of Primley House, Paignton, and Founder of Paignton Zoo, was both a philanthropist and keen plantsman. He found a blue form of the Common Mallow, *Malva sylvestris*, which he propagated at his Primley Botanic Nursery and called 'Primley Blue'.

Though resembling the wild plant in its vigorous and sprawling appearance, as a garden plant it has a longer season of flowering, with masses of lovely smoky-blue blooms, with dark veinings, each about 1½ in. (4 cm) across. 'Primley Blue' is reasonably perennial and readily increases by soft cuttings, taken in summer, and will often layer itself, though the resulting plants can be very misshapen.

The wild plant of common mallow, with its pale to dark pink-purple flowers, is often found on waste places and roadsides. Blue forms that appear identical to 'Primley Blue' have occurred more than once in the wild, including Chudleigh churchyard. Plants increase readily from seed which scatters from the round disk fruits; these fruits look like small cheeses and are often eaten by country children. They are crisp and taste rather like monkey-nuts and in Devon and Cornwall are known as 'Butter and Cheese'.   (PLATE 71)

MUTISIA DECURRENS

This rare and difficult climbing plant from the Chilean and Argentine Andes is often called 'the Climbing Gazania'. It is one of the hardiest and certainly the most striking of this genus in the daisy family. Collected by Richard Pearce, while working for Veitch in 1859, it is a thinly branched tender climber with narrow, undivided, evergreen leaves which are remarkable for extending down the sides of their stems as a pair of narrow wings. The flowers are deep orange or vermilion in colour with yellow centres, 4–5 in. (10–12 cm) in diameter. It received an FCC in 1861, the first year that it flowered.

Mutisia decurrens is an endangered plant, probably because it can easily rot or die from the cold, and young plants are difficult to establish. It has, however, been grown outside on sheltered south-west facing walls, where it can be further protected by climbing through another plant. It likes a cool, moist, shady root run, with a very well-drained soil, and its head in the sun. Though described as evergreen, the stems and leaves usually look dead during the winter.

Propagation is difficult, although seed has germinated readily. The problem is to keep the seedlings healthy. Cuttings, 6–8 in. (15–20 cm) long, without any leaves being removed, have rooted in a shady frame with a little bottom heat. Those that rooted were potted carefully, returned to the frame and given very little water, a regular overhead spraying being given to reduce transpiration and flagging. Only when the roots appear at the sides of the pots can the plants be removed to a cool house.   (PLATE 72)

MYRTUS
Myrtle

The common myrtle has been known in our gardens since the sixteenth century, brought in by traders from the Levant. Of old, it had a mystical connection with love, and by tradition it is often included in brides' wedding bouquets.

In the 1840s, three new species were introduced through the Veitch nursery in Exeter. All fairly tender, the first of these is one of the most rewarding to grow in a sheltered area. *M.luma* (sometimes known as *M.apiculata*) is chiefly desirable for the cinnamon-coloured bark, flaking to reveal a warm cream beneath, in a mature tree; seen in low evening sunlight, it is a beautiful sight. It flowers freely in the late summer, the branches crowded with white flowers, with bosses of yellow stamens, borne singly in the axils of the leaves, later producing masses of dark purple fruits, very attractive to birds; it will sow itself freely in milder gardens. It was found by William Lobb in 1843, growing in the temperate forests of Chile and Argentina.

In 1844, also in the forest regions of Chile, Lobb came across a shrub 5–6 ft (15–18m) high, *M.ugni*, with fragrant rosy-pink flowers in May, later having delicious fruits, darkish purple in colour, which make excellent jam. It is known as the Chilean Guava and was cultivated in the gardens of Valparaiso for dessert; it was said to be Queen Victoria's favourite berry. It grows well in the Isles of Scilly, where the locals call it the Agnus Berry.

The third myrtle introduced by Lobb was *M.chequen*, which grows in damp places, producing an upright, dense, leafy shrub, tree-like in habit, very aromatic, covered with white flowers in late summer. There is a fine specimen at Greenway Gardens, Galmpton.

Myrtles can be trimmed into hedges; there was a mixed species hedge at Dartington, screening the nursery area.   (PLATES 73, 74)

NARCISSUS
Daffodil

The south-west peninsula has some of the best conditions for growing *Narcissus*, with plenty of moisture and deep rich soils. They grow wild in many places; the valley of the Teign provides a breath-taking sight in April, with hundreds of thousands of the native *Narcissus pseudo-narcissus*, 'Lent lilies', massed along the river banks. A corner of a wood near Rattery in south Devon has drifts of a double form that seems like the normal single until one looks inside the trumpet to find that it is full of frilled petaloid segments.

Growers in the West Country have long been able to catch the early flower markets and have sought to raise new varieties. One of the earliest, and probably the best-known, was *N.* 'King Alfred', raised by John Kendall of Newton Poppleford. It had an immediate success, being awarded an FCC in 1899 and marketed in 1900 at ten guineas a bulb – a very high price in those days. Sir Charles Cave of nearby Sidbury Manor raised many cultivars between 1897 and 1932. Two of his award winners were *N.* 'Indus', AM 1932 and *N.* 'Queen of Dawn', AM 1915.

Possibly the most famous Devon grower was E.B. Champernowne, whose nursery overlooks the Tavy Valley near Yelverton. His best-known introduction is probably *N.* 'Red Devon', registered in 1943, which was awarded an AM in 1968 and 1985 and an FCC in 1977. With *N.* 'Fortune' as the seed parent, it flowers early and has a flower 4 in. (10 cm) across with rounded overlapping yellow petals and a short reddish-orange trumpet with a deeper-coloured rim. Other cultivars include *N.* 'Red Lake' – white corona and orange-red trumpet with a deeper-red edge; *N.* 'Queensland' – white corona and salmon-pink cup; *N.*

'Reed Warbler' and 'Burrator'. The nursery was also renowned for the quality of its produce, and boxes of blooms labelled "from E.B. Champernowne" always fetched the highest prices.

Peter Lower, now living in Dawlish, comes from a family of daffodil growers, his father, Dr Nynian Lower, having raised many varieties while living at Presteigne, Radnorshire. He was also instrumental in growing and originally distributing the very popular *Narcissus* 'Fortune', having bought one of the three original bulbs from Walter Ware for £50 in 1917. Nine years later he was selling hundreds at £17 each. After many moves, Peter came to Devon in 1946 where he grew bulbs commercially. He raised the very fine white *Narcissus* 'Askival', registered in 1964. Devon has many other raisers of daffodils, whose plants are listed in this book.   (PLATES 75–77)

NEPENTHES
Pitcher plants

The insectivorous plants have always aroused great interest in Britain especially in the latter part of the nineteenth century when many new species were arriving in this country. They fitted very well with the public's idea of the hazards that intrepid plant hunters had to face: man-eating plants, among vigorous climbers with twining stems and tendrils, that reached out to capture the unsuspecting traveller. Thomas Lobb, collecting for Veitch from the tropical jungles of the Old World, sent *N. albo-marginata*, *N. veitchii*, *N. sanguinea* and other unnamed species to Exeter, and they eventually formed the nucleus of the collection at Chelsea.

John Dominy, then working at Exeter for Veitch, made the first known cross between an unnamed species with green pitchers, believed to be *N. gracilis*, from Borneo, and *N. rafflesiana* which was named *N. × Dominii* after its raiser.

William Court, of Alphington, Exeter, began his gardening career with Lucombe & Pince, transferring to the Exeter branch of Veitch in 1863, and thereafter went to Chelsea, where he was successful in raising many hybrids of both *Nepenthes* and *Sarracenia*.

The Old World Pitcher Plants are famous for their predatory habits. Growing mainly in poor, boggy soils or even on tree trunks, often on mountains, they supplement the meagre fare, obtained through their brittle black roots, with insects caught in elaborate traps or pitchers. Most of the species are herbaceous scramblers. The midrib of the leaf is prolonged into a long tendril, which will coil around any twig it touches, and so support the plant. The tip of the tendril droops down and curls up again at its extreme end in the form of an urn or pitcher. At the top of the pitcher there is an open lid, which prevents the urn from overflowing in tropical rain storms. This is necessary for the plant, as the bottom of the pitcher contains a solution of a protein-breaking enzyme, which dissolves and digests most insects which fall into it. The insects are attracted to the pitchers by perfume and bright colour, commonly red, and by nectar glands inside. To reach the glands they have to pass an overhanging row of spikes above a slippery, smooth band, which cause the insects to fall into the fluid, and which prevent them from escaping.

The plants are not difficult to cultivate, provided that a moist atmosphere is maintained at the relatively expensive and high temperatures of 70–80°F (21–26.5°C) in the summer, and a minimum of 65°F (18.5°C) during the winter. They like a compost consisting of two parts peat to one of sphagnum mixed with a little charcoal. Many like to hang from orchid pots or baskets. Propagation can be by seed, which is a slow process. This is sown thinly on the surface of potting compost that has been very lightly firmed in small pots. Even at temperatures as high as 80°F (26.5°C) germination takes at least four weeks. Seedlings and established plants must always be shaded from direct sunlight and regularly damped down on hot days. (PLATE 78)

NERINE BOWDENII

Few people can have failed to admire, at some time, drifts of the pink-flowered nerines grouped together in a sunny border or under a warm wall. They must be one of the most decorative of autumn-flowering South African bulbs.

Nerine bowdenii, probably the best-known and hardiest of the genus, was found by Athelstan Hall Cornish-Bowden, third son and seventh child of Admiral and Mrs William Cornish-Bowden of Newton Abbot. He came upon the plant in 1898 as a young man of twenty-seven in South Africa where he had a flourishing surveying practice. He was later to become Surveyor General of Cape Colony, and modern Capetown was largely built to his plans. He was an ardent plant-lover and discovered the bulbous plants growing in almost inaccessible situations in the mountains of Cape Colony. He sent a few bulbs home and some were presented to Kew. When it flowered it was recognized as a new and exciting species, was named after the introducer and granted an Award of Merit by the RHS in 1904.

A year later, Mr Cornish-Bowden revisited the mountains and collected yet more bulbs; almost all were sent to the nursery of Mr Old at Newton Abbot who described *Nerine bowdenii* in his catalogue in these words:

The illustration portrays the extremely delicate colour and form of this lovely flower much better than I can describe. It is remarkable for the size of its flower, from six to twelve in an umbel, on a stem 15–18 inches long. In colour, a beautiful Rose Pink with a deeper tint down the middle of each segment. I should be glad to give you any other information respecting this beautiful and rare flower, and will send cultural directions with each order. It is easily grown and only requires a cool frame or conservatory with no other heat than is necessary to exclude frost.

Bulbs were sold at prices ranging from 3s.6d. to 7s.6d. according to weight and size. Some special sizes in pots sold for as much as 10s.6d. – a quite considerable sum in those days.

Today's bulbs can be grown out of doors in a well-drained sunny spot, often at the foot of a south-facing wall where they can be left undisturbed. Should the clumps become too thick and the flowering poor, they should be lifted and divided before they are due to flower. It is recommended that bulbs are planted 6 in. (15 cm) deep, but they will quickly push up to the surface where they benefit from the warmth of the sun. In cold districts winter protection may be needed as the leaves, that follow flowering, and the bulbs tolerate only a few degrees of frost.

Propagation is by division or from the fleshy seeds which germinate rapidly and which are best sown on the surface of the soil. So eager is the seed to germinate that this often takes place even before they have been dispersed from the seed head. This ease of propagation has encouraged the production of many hybrids. Terry Jones from Zeal Monachorum has raised: 'Zeal Damson' – deep damson-red; 'Zeal Plush' ('Aurora' × *N.bowdenii*) – large dusky purplish-pink; 'Zeal Giant' – large deep pink; 'Marney Rogerson' – a pale salmon-pink, selected by Dr Rogerson in his garden at Croyde, North Devon.

Veitch's, before 1919, were impressed with this member of the Daffodil (Amaryllidaceae) family and raised 'Exonia' by crossing *N. bowdenii* with *N. sarniensis (fothergillii)*–scarlet.
(PLATES 80–82)

PLATE 63
Magnolia campbellii 'Sidbury'
at Sidbury Manor

PLATE 64
Magnolia campbellii 'Sidbury'
at Castle Hill, Sidbury

PLATE 65
Magnolia × veitchii 'Peter Veitch'
at Robert Veitch & Son, Exminster

PLATE 66
Magnolia × veitchii 'Peter Veitch'
at Robert Veitch & Son, Exminster

PLATE 67
Magnolia × veitchii 'Isca'
at Robert Veitch & Son, Exminster

PLATE 68
Magnolia × soulangiana 'Coimbra'
at The Garden House

PLATE 69
Mahonia 'Buckland'
at The Garden House

PLATE 70
Mahonia 'Lionel Fortescue'
at The Garden House, Buckland Monachorum

PLATE 71
Malva sylvestris 'Primley Blue'
at Keeper's Cottage, Deancombe

PLATE 72
Mutisia decurrens
at Wisley

PLATE 73
Myrtus luma
at Coleton Fishacre, Kingswear

PLATE 74
Myrtus ugni
at Bicton College, East Budleigh

PLATE 75
Narcissus 'Red Devon'
at du Plessis Bros Nursery,
Landulph, Saltash

PLATE 76
Narcissus 'Queensland', 'Dawn Mist',
'Sarah' from E.B. Champernowne Nursery,
Yelverton

PLATE 77
Narcissus pseudo-narcissus
(double form) at Rattery

PLATE 78
Nepenthes sp. at Ness Gardens,
University of Liverpool

ORCHIDS IN DEVON – PAST AND PRESENT
by Brian and Wilma Rittershausen

Devon has a long history of orchid growing. In Exeter the famous nurseries of Veitch won acclaim for their new introductions of tropical orchids, as well as many other plants and trees, from the 1840s until they moved their orchid nursery to London some time between 1852–5. Their head orchid grower, John Dominy, produced the first orchid hybrid in Exeter by crossing two species, *Calanthe masuca* × *furcata*, named *C.* Dominii. This flowered in October 1856. The method of fertilizing orchids had been shown to him by John Harris, a surgeon at Wonford Hospital, Exeter. The large country estates of that era all had their prized orchid houses. At Bicton in east Devon the first *Odontoglossum* was flowered in 1836 and named *O. bictoniense*.

With the moving of Veitch's to their London nursery, Devon had to wait another one hundred years before other commercial establishments were set up. In 1950 Burnham Nurseries Ltd were importing and growing orchids at a small family-run nursery in Kingsteignton, Newton Abbot. Today they have grown and moved to larger premises at Forches Cross, Newton Abbot, where they house one of the widest selections of orchids in Europe. In 1951, once again thousands of orchids were being raised from seed in Exeter, this time by Ebford Gardens owned by Mr Gordon Ford who worked from his own laboratory, with the help of Exeter University and of his manager Mr Pierce.

Interest in orchids by the average gardener was growing fast at this time, and in 1953 the Devon Orchid Society was founded. Today they hold monthly meetings in Teignmouth, have their own shows and host weekend congresses for the British Orchid Council.

Orchids of note in Devon include:

Cattleya aclandiae

This species is from the bifoliate (two-leaved) section of the genus. Plants have slender pseudobulbs and grow to about 5 in. (12 cm) high, making it one of the smallest in the genus. The flowers are 3–4 in. (7–10 cm) in diameter, fleshy, with a basic colouring of yellowish-green overlaid with patches of dark black purple. The lip is white, tipped with bright rose-purple.

An epiphyte, it orginated from Bahia on the coast of Brazil, growing on isolated trees in the arid lands, exposed to sea breezes. It was introduced in 1839 by Lt James of H.M.S. *Spey* and dedicated to Lady Acland of Killerton, Exeter, where it first flowered. Unfortunately, no record of the plant exists at Killerton today. Now considerably scarce in cultivation, and its importation strictly curtailed, numerous colourful hybrids have been produced from it since 1863. The first was *C.* Brabantiae (*C. aclandiae × loddigesii*) made by Veitch. It is recorded that this was the first orchid hybrid to receive an award from the Royal Horticultural Society. It was given a Silver Banksian Medal and a First Class Certificate in 1863.

It is a vigorous grower, having two growing and flowering seasons each year. The first flowering is usually early summer, with a second in the autumn as the new pseudobulbs are completed. It grows best in an intermediate greenhouse (minimum night temperature 55°F, 13°C) in good light close to the glass, and needs to be kept well watered. (All epiphyte orchids grow best in a bark-based compost.) It will also grow on a piece of cork bark, when its fleshy aerial roots will cling to the bark holding the plant secure. (PLATE 83)

Odontoglossum bictoniense

This species belongs to a large and superior genus of New World orchids. Pseudobulbs with leaves up to 12 in. (30 cm) long, the flower stems are tall and upright, with up to twenty flowers, evenly spaced and facing one way. The sepals and petals are yellowish-green with chestnut-brown barrings. The heart-shaped lip may be white or pale rose. This is a highly variable species which at one time included a number of recognized varieties, named after the specific colouring, e.g. var. *album* and var. *sulphureum*. The plant blooms in the autumn and the flowers last for three to four weeks.

This was the first *Odontoglossum* to arrive in England alive. It was discovered by Mr George Ure-Skinner in Guatemala and sent to Lord Rolle of Bicton in 1835; it flowered for the first time in this country the following year. Later, it was found in abundance in Mexico and became a very popular plant due to its ease of culture and attractive flowers. Although wild plants are no longer imported, this species is still in cultivation as the plant grows and divides easily. Many exciting new hybrids have recently been raised, producing a unique blend of colourings and flower shapes, which have proved its worth as a parent.

It is a cool house plant, growing well in a greenhouse or indoor situation. It enjoys a sunny aspect with plenty of moisture at the roots. Being epiphytic, it will also grow on a tree branch or similar structure. (PLATE 84)

Odontioda Honiton Lace

This is a hybrid raised in 1980 by Burnham Nurseries Ltd of Newton Abbot. The parents are *Odontoglossum trilobum* and *Odontioda* Carisette. The former, a little-known but highly attractive species from Peru, had not previously been hybridized. It passed on to *Odontioda* Honiton Lace its large flower spike habit with up to one hundred blooms. The other parent was a bright red hybrid, which emphasized the colouring in *O.* Honiton Lace and produced a bigger flower. *O.* Honiton Lace has a creamy background with red lacy markings on the sepals and petals. The shape of the lip is also dominated by the species.

Odontioda Honiton Lace 'Burnham' has proved to be an exceptional plant. It received an Award of Merit from the Royal Horticultural Society in 1984, when the votes were unanimous. When shown in the USA, the clone 'J.E.M.' also proved a winner and was given an award by the American Orchid Society in 1980. In addition to growing well in England, it has proved to be 'heat tolerant', making it possible to grow in warmer climates, and it is equally at home in Florida where it has become an extremely popular plant.

In Britain it grows with the inbred hybrid vigour, producing excellent plants which bloom in the early summer. The flower spike can be 5 ft (over 1.5 m) long, with up to one hundred blooms on side branches, the whole stem arching gracefully.   (PLATE 79)

PLATE 79
Odontioda 'Honiton Lace' at Burnham Nurseries, Kingsteignton

ORIGANUM 'Buckland'
Marjoram

The genus *Origanum* consists mainly of Mediterranean sub-shrubs or herbaceous perennials, and this hybrid, *O.* 'Buckland', occurred as a natural cross between *O. amanum* and *O. tournefortii* at The Garden House, Buckland Monachorum. It is reasonably hardy, one parent coming from Turkey and the other from the Island of Amorgos in the Aegean. A small, compact sub-shrub, its leaves are grey-felted and not so woolly as *O. tournefortii*. The flowering spikes are distinctive with pale pink flowers surrounded by striking purplish-pink bracts. About 9 in. (22 cm) high, it makes a delightful plant for the rock garden or when grown in a pot, liking full sun and flowering from July to September.   (PLATE 85)

PASSIFLORA ANTIOQUIENSIS and 'Exoniensis'
Passion flower

The two distinguished Exeter nurseries of Lucombe, Pince & Co. and Veitch can claim full credit for both these lovely passion flowers.

Passiflora mollissima was introduced in 1843. A vigorous climber, it has large, deeply three-lobed leaves and, from nearly every leaf base, pink flowers 3 in. (7.5 cm) across. Collected from tropical South America, it needed the shelter of a large cool greenhouse when brought back to grow in Britain.

In 1858 Lucombe, Pince & Co. were the first to cultivate another Passion flower. Collected in Bogotá, Colombia, the new plant, *Passiflora antioquiensis*, had flowers up to 5 in. (12 cm) across, hanging like parachutes on fine stems. The colour was much stronger, a rich rosy-crimson, with a small violet ring round the centre. This species, too, needed greenhouse protection in Britain, except for very warm protected spots in the far west and the Isles of Scilly.

Only a few years later, the neighbouring Veitch nursery crossed *P. antioquiensis* with *P. mollissima* to produce 'Exoniensis'. The flower of this hybrid is 5 in. (12 cm) across, of a delicate pink, with a small whitish ring round the centre.

The plants are excellent for a cool conservatory and quickly cover rafters, walls and pillars. Too much heat reduces flowering, as does growing in too rich a soil and pruning heavily and too often. John Innes No. 1 with good drainage is recommended for pots and other large containers.
(PLATES 86, 87)

PLATE 80
Nerine bowdenii
at Kiln House, Brixham

PLATE 81
Nerine 'Zeal Giant'
at Hoggetts, Zeal Monachorum

PLATE 82
Nerine 'Zeal Plush'
at Kiln House, Brixham

PLATE 83
Cattleya aclandiae 'Simla Gem'

PLATE 84
Odontoglossum bictoniense

PLATE 85
Origanum 'Buckland'
at Keeper's Cottage, Deancombe

C. Rogers

PLATE 86
Passiflora antioquiensis
at Overbecks, Salcombe

J. Lloyd

PLATE 87
Passiflora × 'Exoniensis'
at Forde Abbey, Dorset

M. Feesey

PLATE 88
Pennisetum alopecurioides 'Woodside'
at RHS, Wisley

J. Lloyd

PLATE 89
Philesia magellanica
at Trengwainton, Cornwall

PENNISETUM ALOPECUROIDES 'Woodside'

Not many gardeners have a love of grasses and their relatives, but Mervyn Feesey is an exception, having an outstanding collection of these, as well as many tender or unusual plants in his garden at Woodside, Barnstaple. This discerning gardener and architect, in his capacity as Hon. County Organiser (Devon) of the National Gardens Scheme, has persuaded many owners to open their gardens to the public.

During August or September, visitors to the RHS Gardens at Wisley, when walking towards the restaurant, will have noticed a densely tufted, perennial grass with slender erect stems. The arching feathery flower plumes are cylindrical and 2–8 in. (5–20 cm) long and, when the bristly inflorescence is fully developed, it is pinkish and 1¼ in. (3–5 cm) wide. 'Woodside' is an exceptionally fine form of this plant and received an Award of Merit in 1971. It flowers more readily than the parent type, without the usual need for warm sunny weather. Propagation is by division.   (PLATE 88)

PHILESIA MAGELLANICA

The French naturalist Philibert Commerson, on de Bougainville's voyage around the world, discovered this shrub in the Magellan region of South America. However, it was William Lobb, collecting for Veitch in 1847, in the Valdivia province of Chile, 800 miles (1300 km) or so to the north, who sent plants back to England, thereby introducing the plant to discerning gardeners.

In the wild the plant's dense sucker-growths are up to 4 ft (1.25 m) high, although it will climb up mossy rocks and tree trunks. It grows naturally in high rainfall forests, sometimes in boggy soils, and must therefore be grown in our gardens in humid, moist, acid soil, rich in humus, on a lightly shaded, cool site. The leaves are dark evergreen, narrowed by inrolled edges, stiff and hard, with a bluish-white beneath. The undoubted beauty comes from the solitary flowers, 2–2½ in. (5–6 cm) long, of rich rosy-crimson, closely resembling its relative *Lapageria*. It was awarded an AM in 1937. *Philesia* was named from the Greek *phileo* – to love – by Commerson, perhaps because the manservant he took on his expeditions was really Jeanne Baret, his mistress, in disguise.

It was at Veitch's Chelsea nursery in 1872 that a hybrid between *Lapageria rosea* (as the seed bearer) and *Philesia* flowered. This bi-generic hybrid × *Philageria veitchii*, needs similar conditions to *Philesia*, where it will scramble and often flower. The plant is rare, and while it is possible for it to survive outside in sheltered places in Devon, Cornwall and other favoured parts of the country, it is better to plant it in a cool house, possibly one used for cool ferns, where it can remain undisturbed. It is slow in growth and to flower, taking perhaps ten years, but well worth the wait.   (PLATE 89)

PRIMULA 'Buckland Wine'

E.B. Champernowne's nursery at Buckland, near Yelverton, was not only known nationwide for breeding and marketing daffodils, but also as a major supplier of *Primula juliae* hybrids. They found an exceptionally good, wine-red flowered plant which they increased in the open fields overlooking the Tavy valley, and it was named 'Buckland Wine'.   (PLATE 90)

PRIMULA 'Harry Adams'

The vagaries of fashion apply equally to plants, sometimes with fatal results. At present primulas that are related to primroses and auriculas are very much in vogue, although they have been grown in cottage gardens for a long time. Unfortunately, many of the older varieties have disappeared despite the efforts of enthusiasts in searching old gardens and nurseries.

One such enthusiast was the late Harry Adams who combined a scientific training with a passion for sea fishing and a love and skill for gardening. He left behind a large garden in Surrey when, in 1974, he moved with his wife to Teignmouth in Devon. His smaller garden soon became a Mecca for gardeners and plantsmen who could share his love of plants and enthusiasm. One wonders how many of his fishing companions, whilst sitting in his front garden, dining on some of the day's catch, were held spellbound by his knowledge and became 'hooked' on gardening.

The rich red Devon loam and the mild climate changed many of his alpines into "cabbages". So he systematically altered his range of plants to include those more suited to the micro-climate of his new home. Among these were various primrose species and cultivars. In 1982, Harry gave Terry Underhill a seedling he had raised from the deliberate crossing of *Primula* 'Garryarde Guinevere' and the wild primrose, *Primula vulgaris*; it was unknown which was the seed-bearing parent. The seedling grew fast, showing symptoms of hybrid vigour, and within two years was a clump over 14 in. (35 cm) across. The foliage has the typical shape of a strong, vigorous primrose. However, the base of the leaf blade and leaf stalk have more purple tints than the common wild primrose, hardly surprising when one looks at the foliage colour of *P.* 'Garryarde Guinevere'. Yet the habit is not of the polyanthus type, being single stemmed, and the long flower stem ends in a purple calyx. The flower is similar in colour to the soft pink of *P.* 'Garryarde Guinevere', but a little larger. The centre of each flower is strongly marked with shades of egg-yolk and pale yellow. The flowers are pin-eyed. An outstanding feature of the blooms is the crinkled petals, slightly overlapping, emitting a delicious scent. The flower lasts a long time but fades with age and long periods of exposure to sunlight. The original clone started flowering in an east-facing border at the turn of the year and stopped producing new blooms only after more than sixteen weeks. Even then it remained for a couple of weeks covered in a mass of almost white flowers with golden centres.

Tragically, a fishing accident brought an untimely end to Harry's life, but we now can have in our gardens this useful harbinger of spring, *Primula* 'Harry Adams', to remind us of that very generous man.   (PLATE 91)

PRIMULA VULGARIS 'Pridhamsleigh'

Cavers from all parts of the British Isles travel to Buckfastleigh to wriggle, crawl and slide down into the limestone depths of the Pridhamsleigh caves, while the traffic roars above them on the busy A38.

In 1967, quietly growing in a nearby leafy lane amidst all this frantic activity, was a truly double form of the wild primrose. It was discovered, nestling between two granite boulders, by Mrs Charles Hillard. Just in time, she rescued the plant to cherish it elsewhere before the tranquillity of the lane was destroyed when bulldozers arrived to carve out the new dual carriageway.

Every year the first flowers to appear are single, arousing fears that it has disappeared, when suddenly the second flush, which comes a little later than the ordinary primrose, opens into full double flowers, with the reproductive organs turned into petals. The colour is the same pure primrose yellow and it keeps its colour well.

Ironically, the plant is not the easiest to establish and plants sent to many gardens, including Kew and Wisley, have failed to survive. Even in gardens in the primrose county of Devon, they have curled up their toes and died but, if they find a spot to their liking, they grow with vigour, making large clumps that can be easily divided. They should be divided and replanted as soon as possible after the flowers have faded.

A rich, moderately heavy loam in an open site, but which is partially shaded from the strong midday sun, suits this exceedingly rare Devon native that many botanists had believed to be lost.

There are many other double primroses available from specially bred seed, but the clue to the genuine 'Pridhamsleigh' is its exact likeness to ordinary *Primula vulgaris* until the bonus of double flowers appears.

(PLATE 92)

PRUNUS DOMESTICA 'Dittisham Plum'

Many of the valleys of the West Country are so sheltered that they became special vegetable- and fruit-growing areas. The Dittisham valley leading to the River Dart was once renowned for its own type of plum. Naming was local and, as well as 'Dittisham Plum', it has been called just 'Dittisham', 'Dittisham Small Red' and 'Dittisham Ploughman' (it is said that 'Ploughman' comes from the German word for plums – Pfläumen). A chance seedling 'Kea' was found and grown near Truro, Cornwall, and is said to be indistinguishable from the Dittisham plums.

At one time there were thirty to forty growers with small orchards of only a quarter to two acres (under 0.8 hectares), making a total of some 20 acres (8 hectares). The fruit was marketed mainly in Dartmouth and Torquay. Today, very few Dittisham plum trees remain, as orchards give way to demands for building land.

Trees are increased by suckers and not by budding or grafting. They quickly attain the size of a bushy small tree and need to be pruned regularly in early life to achieve a strong stem or trunk.

The fruit, normally picked by the first and second weeks of August, is not unlike a roundish 'Victoria', red in colour and juicy. It is not classified as of dessert flavour, but is nevertheless very tasty. It makes jam and preserves of great quality and colour, without the almond flavour associated with 'Victoria'. Its flesh separates freely from the stone.

(PLATE 93)

QUERCUS × *HISPANICA* 'Lucombeana'
Lucombe oak

"I took a ride to St Thomas's, near Exeter, to see a new species of Oak called the Lucombe Oak – from the name of the person who first observed and propagated it", so wrote John Claxton in 1774 to Sir William Lee.

In fact, William Lucombe is known to have planted many Holm oaks before he started his own nursery at St Thomas's in 1720. In about 1763 it is known that he sowed some acorns gathered from a Turkey oak, *Q.cerris*, and noticed that one of the seedlings retained its leaves throughout the winter, and showed signs of vigour. It was probably a hybrid with a Cork oak, *Q.suber*, growing nearby. It grew quickly and was increased by the thousand by grafting on to Turkey oak rootstocks. Some of the original reached about 35 ft (10 m) in eleven years, with straight trunks and corrugated bark. This is Lucombe's oak. It grows to about 100 ft (30 m) with spreading branches upswept at the ends and thick saddle-like bases. The leaves last well into spring, unless the weather is very severe. The timber is fine and close-grained, pale yellowish-brown, and might be a valuable fast-growing hardwood were it not for its uneconomic propagation.

Seedlings grown from the original clone by William Lucombe's son in 1792 showed considerable variations in vigour, evergreenness and shape, and in the corkiness of the bark. The resulting trees have been often distributed, erroneously, under the name of Lucombe oak. Professor Caldwell of Exeter University believed that a particularly fine specimen, still growing on the campus, near Thomas Hall, was one of the original graftings. There are trees of the true clone at Bicton, Exeter University, Ugbrooke, Dartington and elsewhere in the West Country.

The original plant was cut down by William Lucombe senior when it was about twenty years old and some 3ft (1 m) in girth. He had it cut into planks and carefully stored under his bed, where it remained for several years before fulfilling its planned purpose as a coffin for the old gentleman, when he was laid to rest at the remarkable age of 102.

The following are seedlings of the Lucombe oak, raised at Lucombe's Exeter nursery:

'Crispa', called the New Lucombe Oak, was raised in 1792 by the younger William Lucombe. The bark is corky, and the dark green leaves are whitish underneath, with rather crispy edges.

'Dentata', raised in 1830 by Lucombe, Pince & Co., has a corkier bark than its parent. It has large evergreen leaves.

'Heterophylla' has leaves of different shapes, the middle of some reduced to a strip about ¼ in. (6 mm) wide. It was raised about 1830 by Lucombe, Pince & Co.

'Suberosa', raised in 1792, has 2 in. (5 cm) thick corky bark, and small leaves. The original tree, at the entrance to the St Thomas Nursery, was cut down in 1903. The tree by the chapel at Killerton is probably 'Suberosa'.
(PLATES 94, 95)

RHODODENDRON

In the introduction and raising of rhododendron, Devon has played an important part. Lucombe, Pince & Co. of Exeter listed many hybrids, although most of them are now superseded and no longer available. Veitch formed a wonderful collection of Asiatic species, especially the group from Malaya and Java, through the work of Thomas Lobb; these became the parents of many beautiful greenhouse hybrids in the late nineteenth century. (Thomas Lobb also collected plants from the Himalayas.) His brother William, also working for Veitch, collected seed of *R. occidentale* from North America, while in the 1880s Thomas Luscombe of Kingsbridge was working on *R. fortunei*. Almost a century later, Lionel Fortescue of The Garden House, Buckland Monachorum, was to produce many fine hybrids, more of which are still to be registered. Today the painstaking task of raising new hybrids, especially for the smaller garden, is being carried out by, among others, Barry Starling from near Drewsteignton, and Terry Jones, a well-known plantsman from Zeal Monachorum.

The following are illustrated: (PLATES 96-100)

Rhododendron occidentale
The Western Azalea was introduced by Veitch in Exeter, about 1851, from seed collected by William Lobb in light woodlands on the west side of the Rockies in California. It is a 10 ft (3 m) high deciduous shrub, with shining leaves, somewhat glaucous and downy below. It is a valuable plant for its good autumn leaf colour, as well as its fragrant flowers in June. These are wide and funnel-shaped, creamy-white to pale pink, with pale yellow to orange-yellow basal stains. It was awarded an AM in 1944. Perfectly hardy, it is the parent of many beautiful hybrids.

PLATE 90
Primula 'Buckland Wine'
at Feebers Cottage, Broadclyst

PLATE 91
Primula 'Harry Adams'
at Fairlight, Rattery

PLATE 92
Primula vulgaris 'Pridhamsleigh'
at Keeper's Cottage, Deancombe

PLATE 94
Quercus × *hispanica* 'Lucombeana'
at Thomas Hall, University of Exeter

PLATE 93
Prunus domestica 'Dittisham Ploughman'
at Hill Quay, Ashprington

PLATE 95
Quercus × hispanica 'Lucombeana'
at County Hall, Exeter

PLATE 96
Rhododendron occidentale
at Dartington Hall, near Totnes

PLATE 97
Rhododendron 'Luscombei'

PLATE 98
Rhododendron glaucophyllum 'Len Beer'
at Drewsteignton

PLATE 99
Rhododendron 'Katharine Fortescue'
at The Garden House, Buckland Monachorum

PLATE 100
Rhododendron 'Zeal Doubloon'
at Hoggetts, Zeal Monachorum

Rhododendron 'Luscombei'

Thomas Luscombe, who lived at Lower Coombe Royal, Kingsbridge, used the highly fragrant *R. fortunei* to create several new hybrids at the end of the nineteenth century. Crossing it with the rich blood-red and earlier flowering *R. thomsonii*, he produced *R.* 'Luscombei' and 'Luscombei Splendens'. *R.* 'Luscombei' has loose trusses of trumpet-shaped flowers of deep rose with a ray of crimson markings inside. It grows into a large bush or small tree, 15 ft (5 m) and twice as wide, and is found in many large gardens in Britain, where it makes an attractive woodland specimen. It may be a good parent, being used in countless other crosses, but it is not a good commercial plant, being difficult to root and slow to come into bloom. An enormous tree, still growing in the gardens at Lower Coombe Royal, is possibly the original *griffithianum* cross, believed to have been raised by Luscombe and named *R.* 'Coombe Royal'. The flowers, in large trusses, are rose pink in bud, opening to white with a central crimson pattern. It received an AM in 1900 when shown by Robert Veitch & Son of Exeter.

Rhododendron glaucophyllum 'Len Beer'

Len Beer, brought up in Ivybridge, was trained at the Dartington Hall Gardens. While employed as a horticulturalist at the University College of North Wales, he led, in 1971, an expedition to a little-known area of Nepal. Together with Roy Lancaster and Dave Morris, he was exploring the Barun Khola, a high valley on the approach to Makalu, 28 000 ft (9122 m), when they discovered a form of *R. glaucophyllum* in seed, which they collected. In the course of time the seedlings flowered and proved to be consistently white. The best of these seedlings was selected for exhibition at the 1977 Chelsea Flower Show where it received an Award of Merit. Sadly, Len never knew of this, for he had died of cancer, at the age of thirty-five, the previous year. In honour of Len, who was a great character and plantsman, this excellent plant bears his name.

R. glaucophyllum 'Len Beer' is a compact, slow-growing, dwarf shrub reaching little more than 18 in. (45 cm) in height and about the same across. The elliptic leaves are matt-green above and silvery beneath, while the flower trusses may contain up to ten snow-white bells about 1 in. (2.5 cm) long.

Rhododendron 'Katharine Fortescue'

Lionel Fortescue made many crosses of rhododendrons at The Garden House, ably assisted by his gardeners who included the late Bill Robins and Michael

Hickson, now Head Gardener at Knightshayes. Chief among these is the lovely hybrid pictured here – *R.* 'Katharine Fortescue' (*R.* 'Hawk' × *R. griffithianum*), which is now a large vigorous shrub, about 8 × 6 ft (2.5 × 2 m) and very free-flowering. In April the trusses have about eight funnel-shaped flowers, greeny-yellow, paling to cream at the margins. It received an AM in 1981. This beautiful plant is a lasting tribute to the memory of an outstanding plantsman who was always willing to pass on his skills and knowledge to others, and to his wife who was also a very knowledgeable gardener and an excellent hostess to their countless visitors.

Rhododendron 'Zeal Doubloon'
This hybrid has been raised by Terry Jones, another of Devon's present-day outstanding plantsmen. In his garden at Zeal Monachorum, near Crediton, he created an unusual hybrid between *R.* 'Crest' and *R.* 'Tortoiseshell Orange'. It is a 'hose-in-hose', with bell-shaped flowers of a strong clear yellow.

ROSA 'Devoniensis'

Devon can claim the distinction of being the home of the first tea rose bred in England. G. Foster of Devonport, Plymouth, made the cross between 'Smith's Yellow' and 'Park's Yellow' in 1838 to produce *Rosa* 'Devoniensis', which was introduced by Lucombe, Pince & Co. of Exeter in 1841.

The original bush type grew some 4 ft (1.25 m) high and its very cream-white flowers were flushed apricot on opening and at the centres. The Reverend Joseph Pemberton in 1920, in his book *Roses, their History and Development*, said of 'Devoniensis', "its delicious tea-scent – the real thing, surpassed by none – brought rosarians to their knees". It blossomed several times a year but was very tender and it is believed that the bush type has disappeared.

Samuel Pavitt at his nursery at Bathwick, near Bath had, however, found that some of the 'Devoniensis' he had budded on an *R.* 'Céline' rootstock produced 3–9 ft (1–3 m) shoots in a season, and were hardy. Against a house one of these plants reached 40 ft (12 m) high and half as wide. It is generally known as 'Climbing Devoniensis' (FCC 1866), and formerly was known as 'the Magnolia Rose'. Pavitt, however, insisted there were not two separate plants, but one cultivar behaving differently according to its rootstock, and it is interesting to note that present-day 'Climbing Devoniensis', on yet other rootstocks, are about

12 ft (4 m) high (and need a warm wall). The plant was introduced by Henry Curtis of the Devon Rosery, Torquay, and is still available.   (PLATE 101)

ROSA 'Weetwood'

Mr and Mrs Harold Bawden are keen plant growers and have lectured nationwide on alpines, dwarf conifers and shrubs and on their various gardens. It comes as a surprise to many who know them to find out that their keenness on breeding and selection of new plants extended into roses. In their garden at Offwell, near Honiton, Mrs Bawden selected a seedling from 'Debutante' in 1983 which they named 'Weetwood'. It is classified as a *Wichuraiana* rambler, with exceptionally strong growth 20–26 ft (6–8 m) and large hanging trusses of delicate pink flowers, each about 2–3 in. (5–7 cm) across and scented.
(PLATE 102)

RUBUS 'Hildaberry'

In 1980 Eric Cornwell of Kennford used a soft brush to transfer pollen from a 'Tayberry' on to another hybrid, the 'Boysenberry', to produce a 'Hildaberry'. The plant was launched at Chelsea in 1987, accompanied by nearly a hundred little pots of delicious jelly made from the fruit by his wife, Hilda, after whom the plant is called.

The 'Hildaberry' is more vigorous than either of its parents, readily producing small thorned stems of 6–9 ft (2–3 m) in length. Typical of the majority of fruits, the large white flowers, often 2–3 in. (5–7 cm) across, and produced from late May to early June, are short lived. Were this not so, the plant could well qualify as a flowering climber, not merely a cane fruit.

The fruits, which are larger than a fifty pence piece, quickly turn very dark red. They are sweet, juicy and excellent for dessert and cooking. Yields are comparable with other good blackberry and hybrid berries, of between 5–15 lb (2.25–7 kg) a plant. Unlike 'Tayberries', the fruit picks easily, parting readily from the calyx. When cooked the core is also far less noticeable than that of the 'Tayberry' and many similar hybrids.

Plants have been grown for a number of years by the RHS at Wisley and were included in the National Fruit Trials at Brogdale Experimental Horticultural Station from 1988. Considerable interest is being aroused by this hybrid among commercial growers. (PLATE 103)

SAXIFRAGA 'Dartington Double'

One of the many plants that originated from Dartington Hall Trust's Nursery is *Saxifraga* 'Dartington Double'. There are no details of its origin. It is a neat mossy saxifrage, bearing double pink flowers during April and May. As with many other members of the mossy section, it prefers a semi-shaded position where it will not dry out. Though it grows to a height of a mere 3 in. (7 cm), it will spread as rapidly as any of its taller counterparts.   (PLATE 104)

SCHIZOSTYLIS COCCINEA 'Zeal Salmon'
Kaffir lily

Probably one of the most appreciated plants from South Africa which brightens beds and borders in many Devon gardens in late summer and autumn is *Schizostylis coccinea*. Enjoying streamsides in its native habitat, it thrives in most garden soils, preferring moisture and a sunny aspect. The climate of Devon is usually ideal for a plant that can be severely checked in its growth by hard winters in less favoured parts of the country. A welcome addition to the range of cultivars/hybrids is *S.* 'Zeal Salmon', with deep salmon-pink flowers, larger than most, appearing in September, October and often into November and beyond. This hybrid of *S.* 'Mrs Hegarty' and Eric Smith's *S.* 'Sunrise' was raised by Terry Jones of Zeal Monachorum, near Crediton. This excellent plantsman manages to grow and raise a wide range of plants to perfection on a very heavy soil, which would not suit most gardeners.

The Kaffir lily's freely increasing roots quickly make a dense clump which will readily divide. Some gardeners believe that *Schizostylis* need to be regularly divided and replanted in fresh soil to maintain the production of good flowering stems, although many a fine clump, enjoying a good Devon loam, has been left to flourish undisturbed for a number of years.   (PLATE 105)

SEQUOIADENDRON GIGANTEUM
Wellingtonia · Big tree

Almost every large estate has one or more of these enormous trees, said to be among the tallest in the world. They are only found naturally in isolated groups on the western slopes of the Sierra Nevada, California, where they can grow to over 340 ft (105 m) in height and 83 ft (27 m) in trunk girth and can live for up to 3400 years. Their tall conical shape makes them very distinctive.

In 1853 two introductions of seed were made. John Mathew sent seeds to his father Patrick, in Perthshire, but the more important despatch was by William Lobb to Veitch at Exeter. Plants, raised from this introduction, were in their final positions within eighteen months of seed collection from the wild. The tree is hardy in Britain, prefers deep soil and a sheltered site, and dislikes shade.

Though never used widely for timber as the wood is brittle with little strength, light in weight, soft and spongy, it is utilized for fencing, limited constructional purposes and for shingles. The 'Big Tree' aroused such interest in the public's imagination, that it was suggested it should be named *Wellingtonia gigantea*, after the Iron Duke, instead of the Cherokee name of See-qua-yah. Despite the counter-claims of many Americans to name it 'Washingtonia', after their own great general, they did not succeed, as this was already the name of a palm. In 1939 botanists separated it from *Sequoia sempervirens* into a distinct genus, renaming it *Sequoiadendron giganteum*. In 1970 the tallest specimen known in Britain, 165 ft (51 m), was at Endsleigh, near Tavistock. (PLATE 106)

SISYRINCHIUM STRIATUM 'Aunt May'

The lady who gave her name to several good forms of garden plants was the creator of the garden at Chevithorne, near Tiverton, and also the aunt of Sir John Heathcote Amory of Knightshayes Court. Mrs Ludovic Amory, affectionately known as 'Aunt May', was generous with both cuttings and plants, some of which bear her name and some the name of her garden. There is an erysimum, as well as this sisyrinchium, that is named as a tribute to this discerning gardener.

Sisyrinchium 'Aunt May' is a variegated form of the Chilean *S. striatum*. It forms a clump, about 1 ft (30 cm) high, of grey-green iris-like leaves with a wide distinctive striped variegation of creamy yellow. These leaves are fully evergreen but, on the death of a flower shoot, the leaves holding it also wither and die. The flower spikes bear numerous pale straw-yellow flowers, beautifully striped with purple on the reverse of the petals; unfortunately, they are short-lived and fade in the afternoon sun. Propagation is by division in the spring or early autumn. The plant likes a well-drained site of moisture-retentive soil, to reduce the chances of brown withered tips following periods of dry weather, and not too harsh a climate. (PLATE 107)

SORBUS DEVONIENSIS

The small speckled brown fruits of this tree were picked and sold in Barnstaple pannier market up to about 1950. It is locally known as 'French Hales', although *The Flora of Devon* refers to it as 'French Hailes or Hail'. Geoffrey Grigson in *The Englishman's Flora* explains 'French' as a name often given to an unusual or foreign plant, and 'Hales' from 'halse' which is a south-west dialect form of hazel, referring to the shape of the leaf. W.J. Bean (eighth edition), however, suggests that this "is undoubtedly a corruption of the French 'alise' for the fruits of the service trees (*S. latifolia* is 'L'Alisier de Fontainebleau') … Chaucer in *The Romaunt of the Rose* [mentions] 'notes, aleys and bollas' (nuts, hales and bullace)".

Sorbus devoniensis in Devon is found scattered in the north-west and on Haldon Hill, near Exeter, and a few other isolated sites (and in east Cornwall and south-east Ireland), in woods and hedges, usually on well-drained soils. It is very likely that many of the north Devon trees were planted for the sweet and mealy fruits. The 1939 edition of *The Flora of Devon* describes the variability of *Sorbus* × *latifolia*, the broadleaved Whitebeam, of which *Sorbus devoniensis* was thought to be a Devon form. It breeds true from seed and the comparatively narrower leaves are a shining deep green above and greyish-green below. It probably derives from a natural cross between the wild Service tree (*Sorbus torminalis*) and one of the Whitebeam (*Sorbus aria*) relatives, or their progeny.   (PLATE 108)

STREPTOCARPUS MICHELMOREI

Some fifty years ago, Philip Michelmore, a founder member of the Devon NCCPG Group and for many years a Director of Paignton Zoo, was clambering up the near-vertical bank of a stream in Zimbabwe when he discovered a plant growing under evergreen trees and bushes by the River Inyamadzi, near Mount Selinda, Melsetter. It was later to be named after him *Streptocarpus michelmorei*.

The first recording of the plant was made in 1889 in Southern Rhodesia (Zimbabwe) by C.F.M. Swynnerton, of Tsetse fly fame. His herbarium specimen had lain unidentified in the British Museum for many years. When Mr Michelmore rediscovered it in 1937 he had greater success. Herbarium specimens and seed were sent to Kew, who flowered it in the following and subsequent years. Seed was grown by his mother at their Chudleigh home and also at Paignton Zoo.

Streptocarpus michelmorei was first described by B.L. Burtt in 1939 in the *Kew*

PLATE 101
Rosa 'Devoniensis'
at Mottisfont Abbey, Hampshire

PLATE 102
Rosa 'Weetwood'
at Westhill, Ottery St Mary

PLATE 103
Rubus 'Hildaberry'
at Kennford

PLATE 104
Saxifraga 'Dartington Double'
at Southcombe Gardens, Widecombe

PLATE 105
Schizostylis 'Zeal Salmon'
at Little Southey, Northcott

PLATE 106
Sequoiadendron giganteum
at Thomas Hall, University of Exeter

PLATE 107
Sisyrinchium striatum 'Aunt May'
at Keeper's Cottage, Deancombe

PLATE 108
Sorbus devoniensis
at Lee, Ilfracombe

PLATE 109
Streptocarpus michelmorei from
Curtis Botanical Magazine N.S. 54

PLATE 110
Tropaeolum azureum
at Great Dixter, East Sussex

R. Fulcher

PLATE 111
Tropaeolum speciosum
at Myrtle Cottage, Ashprington

A. Baker

PLATE 112
Viola 'Dartington Blue'
at Dartington Hall, near Totnes

A. Baker

PLATE 113
Vitis vinifera 'Mrs Pince'
at RHS, Wisley

W. Halliday

Bulletin. It is one of those curious *Streptocarpus* which, during its lifetime, produces only one single leaf. This leaf is somewhat crinkled and resembles a primrose leaf, but it is continually growing at its base and withering away at its tip. The beauty of its flowers more than compensates for lack of foliage. In the spring and summer, 8–12 in. (20–30 cm) stems rise from the base of the leaf, holding heads of violet flowers. Each bloom is trumpet-shaped with a flared mouth 1¼ in. (3 cm) across, and has a purple patch inside, and a yellow blotch further down, the throat. The flowers are succeeded by long twisted seed pods, so typical of *Streptocarpus*, and they give the genus its name – *streptos* meaning twisted and *karpos*, fruit.

This biennial pot plant needs to be grown afresh from seed each year and artifically pollinated with a paint brush. It is believed to be lost to cultivation, but let us hope it still exists somewhere. B.L. Burtt, who is the naming authority, wrote in *Curtis Botanical Magazine* Vol. 166, "*Streptocarpus michelmorei* is undoubtedly the finest of the recent introductions and indeed bears comparison with any of the known species". (PLATE 109)

TROPAEOLUM

Tropaeolum azureum was discovered in South America by William Lobb on his very first voyage, started in 1840, for Veitch. It is a delicate, tender climber, growing from small tubers, and which in the autumn produces purple-blue nasturtium flowers with yellow centres 1 in. (2.5 cm) across, and each with a ⅖ in. (1 cm) spur. When introduced, it met with instant success and within only a few months had received a Silver Medal from the RHS.

T. azureum dislikes lime and is usually grown in pots of sharply draining turfy loam and peat. In Britain it grows in autumn and winter, needing all possible sunshine and a minimum of 50 °F (10 °C). A trellis or twiggy sticks should be used to support the delicate, hairless annual shoots. When the shoots die down, water should be withheld until growth begins anew; the tubers can then be repotted and watered carefully.

William Lobb came back to Devon in 1844 to renew his contract with Veitch, and in no time at all was back in South America where he travelled as far south as Valdivia, northern Patagonia and the island of Chiloé. He brought back with him a veritable treasure-trove of plants: *Berberis darwinii*, *Embothrium coccineum*, *Escallonia macrantha*, *Lapageria rosea*, *Streptosolen jamesonii* and yet more Tropaeolums. The best known of these is *T. speciosum* or the Flame flower, a hardy perennial climber with brilliant scarlet, long-spurred flowers. To grow well it needs a moist, lime-free soil where its long, creeping, white fleshy underground stems can be undisturbed and kept cool by partial shade. In the right conditions, it makes an excellent climber for north walls or for growing over evergreen trees, shrubs or hedges.

Linnaeus named the common Nasturtium – a less tender relative of this lovely group of plants – *Tropaeolum majus*, from the Latin *tropaeum* and the Greek *tropaion*, meaning trophy. The RHS Dictionary tells us he was reminded, on seeing the flowers growing up pyramids of poles and netting, of the custom in classical times of hanging captured gold helmets, "spear-pierced and bloodstained", from tree trunks set up on the battlefields.   (PLATES 110, 111)

VIOLA 'Dartington Blue'

Dartington Hall Trust, near Totnes, had a very thriving Nursery and Green Crops Department in the 1930s. They introduced many fine plants to the discerning gardener, and through the generosity of the founders, Leonard and Dorothy Elmhirst, distributed many of their treasures to other gardens and horticultural establishments. An unnamed plant of a moderately large, luminous blue-flowered *Viola* was given to nearby Torbay Parks Department in the early 1930s. It is a most striking plant with the clear-coloured open flower having almost no eye. It attracted considerable attention when in full bloom in a large flower bed and was given the name 'Dartington Blue'. There are no records, to date, of the parentage, and therefore origin, of this good garden plant; perhaps it is another cultivar whose name has been lost. Whatever its name, it certainly makes a marvellous display and is just the plant to grow at the foot of the ancient wall of soft grey local stone, by the bowling green at Dartington Hall; very much a case of "the right plant for the right spot".   (PLATE 112)

VIOLA ODORATA
Sweet violet

The violet was one of the first flowering plants to be grown commercially, as, according to Theophrastus, they were being sold in the market in Athens around 400 B.C.

In Devon, however, violets were grown commercially only for local demand until 1891, when two brothers named Westcott, who grew violets at Cockwood, near Starcross, sent a few bunches by train to London and found that the returns were greater than obtained locally. Other pioneer growers were J. Heath and R.W. Beachey at Kingskerswell. The first violet farm was established at Dawlish in 1916, and from then onwards several holdings sprang up in the Teignmouth, Holcombe, Dawlish, Starcross and Kenton areas. By 1926 the number of British violets reaching the markets at least equalled those from France, and the steady expansion continued until 1930, partly due to slight government aid in the form of a tariff on imported flowers. A boom in violet-growing then took place, with a 500 per cent increase in the Dawlish area by 1936.

One of the most enterprising of the new businesses was the Windward Violet Farm and it figures prominently in the history of Devon-raised violets. Founded in 1922 by Mr and Mrs George Zambra, by the 1930s it was growing violets on a considerable scale – between 7000 and 10 000 plants of 'Princesse de Galles' being planted annually. Mrs Zambra also produced perfume, crystallized violets and a violet-flavoured honey from a somewhat vicious strain of bees kept in the garden, which has since been exterminated. To this day, such products are still sought by tourists as a memento of their holiday in Devon. The Zambra family introduced several cultivars, among them 'Pamela Zambra', 'Windward', 'Norah Church' and 'Mrs R. Barton'. Details of these and later introductions will be found in the *Hortus Devoniensis* at the end of this book.

In 1961 the business was sold and trading ceased for a time. In 1967 the Arnot and Moreland families came to live at Windward, part of the time running it as an exclusive guest house. Many people called at the house, either to birdwatch or to visit the wild-flower meadow on the cliff. One such visitor was Roy Coombs, a keen violet grower and author, who called regularly to see what violets were left growing in the garden. He persuaded Mrs Arnot to save what remained of the Zambra violets. She, with her son Robert, began to propagate and market in about 1980, encouraged by Mr Coombs, and her neighbour Mr Leaman, a violet specialist. New cultivars were introduced, such as 'Princess Diana', 'Jean Arnot' and 'Elsie Coombs'. Mrs Arnot made a great contribution to the violet world by saving and distributing many cultivars which would otherwise have been lost, but sadly, she and her sister reluctantly put the Windward Violet Farm on the market in 1984. The present tenant is Edmund Holden, who, in his turn, has propagated many of the violets, with a view to marketing in 1989, encouraged and advised by Mrs Arnot.
(PLATE 114)

1. *V.o.* 'Elsie Coombs'
2. *V.o.* 'Princess Diana'
3. *V.o.* 'Pamela Zambra'
4. *V.o.* 'Jean Arnot'
5. *V.o.* 'Norah Church'
6. *V.o.* 'Windward'
7. *V.o.* 'Mrs R. Barton'

PLATE 114
Viola odorata from the artist's National Collection, near Truro

Yvonne Matthews

VITIS VINIFERA 'Mrs Pince'

Any nursery which listed Capability Brown among its customers must have had a good reputation, and there is evidence that the famous landscaper bought many of his trees from Lucombe's at St Thomas, Exeter. The range of plants expanded throughout the nineteenth century at Lucombe, Pince & Co. and, in 1861, shortly before her death, Mrs Pince of that firm raised a grape vine from a pip which earned a First Class Certificate from the RHS.

When the vine first fruited in 1863, it was realized that 'Mrs Pince's Black Muscat' – as it is often called – had considerable potential as a glasshouse Muscat grape, because it set fruit and ripened under glass without the need for artificial heat – a major problem with other Muscat grapes. It is a long-lasting grape which grows with little attention, but it does take longer to ripen than most others and needs hand pollination.

Read's Nursery, Hales Hall, Loddon, Norfolk, say that "it is an excellent late variety, and has large strong-shouldered and tapering bunches of oval black berries on short rigid stalks. The thick skins of purplish-black with a thin bloom cover a firm, sweet and vinous flesh with a fine Muscat flavour".

As this vine is still available from at least one nursery, there is no reason why this excellent dessert grape should not be grown in place of 'Black Hamburg', providing it will set and ripen without heat today as it did over 125 years ago. (PLATE 113)

Hortus Devoniensis

or

List of

Devon Garden

and Greenhouse Plants

Every plant included in the Hortus Devoniensis belongs to one or more of the following categories:

1. Introduced to this country from the wild, through a Devon nursery or garden.
2. Raised or selected in Devon.
3. Originally found wild in Devon, and brought into cultivation.
4. Called after a well-known Devonian or a Devon gardener.

About half of those mentioned are not available from nurseries, and many are probably no longer in cultivation. National Collections, which have been set up by the NCCPG, and a general interest in propagating and dispersing the uncommon, could have saved most of them.

Awards from the Royal Horticultural Society

AGM	Award of Garden Merit – given for garden use.
AM	Award of Merit – for varieties showing distinct improvement on their predecessors.
FCC	First Class Certificate – for intrinsic excellence.
T after any of above	Award given after a trial at RHS Gardens, Wisley.
Cory Cup	Given for the best man-made hybrid of the year.
VMH	The Victoria Medal of Honour was established "to enable the Council (of the RHS) to confer conspicuous honour on those British horticulturalists, resident in the United Kingdom, whom it might, from time to time, consider deserving of special honour at the hands of the Society".

Veitch Nurseries: some dates

1808	**Veitch & Son** Budlake, Killerton
1832-63	**James Veitch & Son** Mount Radford, Exeter
1863-	**James Veitch & Sons** Chelsea
1864-1931	**Robert Veitch & Son** New North Road, Exeter, Exminster (1864) and Alphington (1931)
1969	Bought from Mildred Veitch by St Bridget Nurseries

Abies (Pinaceae)

bracteata. The Santa Lucia Fir, from the
Californian mountains after which it is
named. In outline conical with a narrow
top, sometimes growing to 120 ft (36 m) in
this country, where late spring frosts are
not too damaging. The needles can be
2½ in. (6.5 cm) long, longer than those of
any other Fir. The cones have long
bristles. Introduced in 1853 by William
Lobb for the Exeter firm of Veitch.
FCC 1915.

lasiocarpa arizonica 'Kenwith Blue'. A
form of the Corkbark Fir selected for its
foliage colour and raised by Gordon
Haddow at Kenwith Castle Nurseries,
Bideford, recently. A dense narrow spire,
likely to reach 60 ft (18 m) in this country.

Abutilon (Malvaceae)

paeoniflorum. Tall shrub. Petals deep
rose-red colour, contrasting with tufts of
bright yellow anthers. Sent by William
Lobb from Brazil and first flowered at
Exeter in 1845.

Acacia (Leguminosae) Wattle

cycnorum. Introduced from the Swan
River area of south-west Australia by
Lucombe & Pince 1852, through their
contract with James Drummond, a farmer
and collector.

'Exeter Hybrid'. See p.30.

siculiformis bossiaeoides. A form of the
Dagger Wattle introduced recently from
the mountains of New South Wales by Dr
J. Smart of Marwood Hill. To 10 ft (3 m)
tall, with small prickly needle leaves and
small pale yellow flower balls.

spectabilis. The White Stem or Mudgee
Golden Wattle. A shrub or small tree
6–20 ft (2–6 m) high with smooth bluish
white bark and finely divided leaves. Bright
yellow flowers in globe heads to ½ in.
across, in branching clusters. From dry or
rocky places in S.E. Australia. It was given
by H.B. Lott to Lucombe, Pince & Co. of
Exeter in 1820.

Acer (Aceraceae)

palmatum 'Buckland Ruby'. Possibly the
best of the red-leaved *Dissectums*, being
more red than purple, and holding its
colour better. Found in a Devon garden in
the 1980s and propagated by S. Pawlowski
of Buckland Monachorum.

Aerides (Orchidaceae). Greenhouse orchids
with waxy fragrant flowers, growing on trees
in the wild, the following species introduced
to Veitch of Exeter by Thomas Lobb:

fieldingii. Fox-brush Orchid. Large white
flowers, mottled with bright pink, trowel-
shaped rose-purple lip; in broad hanging
spikes to 3 ft (1 m) long. Growing on trees
in the wild in Assam. 1850.

fieldingii williamsii. Pale pinkish white
flowers.

multiflorum lobbii. White flowers,
slightly pink edges, few violet spots; lip
deep violet with white centre; in long
pendulous spikes. Burma. 1851.

multiflorum veitchii. White flowers
dotted rose-pink, in hanging branched
clusters.

Aeschynanthus (Gesneriaceae). Trailing,
scrambling or climbing plants, native from
Indonesia to China; needing warmth and
damp when growing, less damp in winter;
mostly growing on trees. Showy tubular
flowers, curved or lipped, usually in clusters,
fragrant and long-lasting. Greenhouse. The
species below were introduced by Thomas
Lobb through Veitch:

cordifolius. About 1 ft (30 cm) high with
deep red flowers striped black, orange
inside. Borneo 1858.

fulgens. About 1 ft (30 cm) high. 2 in.
(5 cm) long bright crimson flowers,
undersides and insides orange, mouth
lined black-purple, October. Indonesia
1855.

lobbianus. Trailing. Fiery red flowers,
cream-yellow inside the mouth; emerging
from "glistening silky soot-red calices",
May to July. Java 1845.

longiflorus. Straggling with hanging shoots. Crimson flowers in the summer. Java 1845.

miniatus. About 1½ ft (45 cm) high. Crimson flowers in June. Java 1845.

pulcher. Royal Red Bugler. Climbing or trailing, with hanging branches. Bright scarlet two-lipped flowers, yellow throats. June. Java 1845.

purpurescens. Java.

radicans. Java 1845.

speciosus. About 2 ft (60 cm) high. 4 in. (10 cm) long flame-orange to scarlet flowers with yellow bases, orange throats with red-brown marks, summer. Java 1845.

'Splendidus'. 3 in. (7.5 cm) long flowers, bright scarlet with black spots on margins. Hybrid raised at Lucombe, Pince & Co. in 1851 by crossing *A. speciosus* with *A. grandiflorus.*

Aesculus (Hippocastanaceae)

californica. The Californian Buckeye is a small Horse Chestnut with fragrant white or slightly pink flowers and large smooth fruit. It was introduced by William Lobb in about 1850 for Veitch of Exeter.

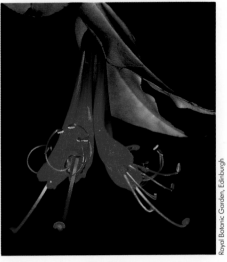

PLATE 115
Aeschynanthus longiflorus

Royal Botanic Garden, Edinburgh

Agalmyla (Gesneriaceae)

staminea. A climber about 2 ft (60 cm) high, with clusters of scarlet tubular flowers in the summer. Warm greenhouse. Introduced from Java by Thomas Lobb in 1846 for Veitch.

Agapanthus (Liliaceae, or more recently Alliaceae) African Lily

'Phantom'. Porcelain-blue flowers changing to milk-white in the throats on about 3 ft (90 cm) stems in the summer. A seedling raised and selected at Coleton Fishacre recently.

Agapetes (Ericaceae). Evergreen shrubs, often growing on trees, native from Nepal to Australia. Showy tubular or urn-shaped waxy flowers in clusters. Lime-free peaty compost.

incurvata. (syn: *Pentapterygium rugosum*) About 3 ft (1 m) high. Hanging flowers nearly 1 in. (2.5 cm) long, white to pink, crossed by irregular dark purple veins, pale yellow mouth. Cool greenhouse or very mild shady spot. Introduced from Assam in 1860 by Thomas Lobb for Veitch. AM 1934.

variegata macrantha (syn: *Thibaudia macrantha*) . To about 6 ft (2 m) tall. Flowers hanging in bunches from the trunk and older branches, 1¾ in. (3.7 cm) long, white to pink with red veins across, tipped white or green. Winter. Greenhouse. Introduced from Burma by Thomas Lobb for Veitch, who first flowered it in 1850. FCC 1860. Sometimes listed as *A. macrantha.*

Agave (Amaryllidaceae)

americana. The Century Plant has large rosettes of leathery succulent leaves to 3 ft (1 m) or more long and yellowish flowers on the side-shoots of a stem to 25 ft (8 m) tall, produced rather less occasionally than the common name describes. Wild in Mexico and naturalized in Mediterranean Europe. It first grew and flowered in the open air in this country in the garden of James Yates at Salcombe in 1814.

PLATE 116
Agave americana at Torquay

Alocasia (Araceae)
lowii veitchii (syn: *A. lowii picta*). Arrow-head green leaves to 16 in. (40 cm) long, with a greyish metallic sheen, wide white veining, and deep purple undersides, on long green striped stalks marked with rose. 'Cuckoo-pint' (Arum) flowers with a whitish green hood. Warm greenhouse. Introduced in 1859 from Borneo by Thomas Lobb for Veitch.

Alstroemeria (Amaryllidaceae)
inodora (syn: *A. nemorosa*). The flowers are in loose clusters at the ends of long stems, yellow, edged red, and with dark markings on the three inner petals. Introduced through William Lobb from the Organ Mountains of Brazil (about 90 miles (55 km) north of Rio de Janeiro), to Veitch of Exeter, where it first flowered under glass in 1841–2.

Aphelandra (Acanthaceae)
nitens. A greenhouse shrublet with lipped vermilion flowers in showy erect spikes in summer; evergreen foliage, bronze with a silver midrib above, and purple below. Grown in pots in light soil in a warm greenhouse. Collected in 1863 in Colombia by Pearce, working for Veitch of Exeter.

Aquilegia (Ranunculaceae)
vulgaris 'Woodside'. A chance seedling of the native Columbine found a few years ago by Mervyn Feesey in his Barnstaple garden. The leaves are strongly mottled cream-yellow; the flowers vary from plant to plant through pinks and purples. It is largely true from seed.

Arachnanthe (Orchidaceae)
lowii. A Spider Orchid to 12 ft (4 m) high with rows of narrow leaves to 2½ ft (75 cm) long; and 3 in. (7.5 cm) wavy yellowish-green flowers covered in chocolate-red blots, borne all along stalks that hang down 6 to 12 ft (2–4 m). Introduced from Borneo in 1845 by Thomas Lobb for Veitch.

Araucaria araucana (Araucariaceae)
See p.30.

Argyranthemum (Compositae)
frutescens 'Overbecks Gold'. A form of the Marguerite or Paris Daisy with deep yellow flowers about 2 in. (5 cm) across for most of the year. Rather shrubby and about 3 ft (1 m) high. Hardy only in the mildest gardens. Found at Overbecks, Salcombe, by Roy Cheek of Cannington in 1984. Often called *Chrysanthemum frutescens* and originally named 'Sharpitor Gold'.

PLATE 117
Aquilegia vulgaris 'Woodside' at Woodside, near Barnstaple

Aristolochia (Aristolochiaceae)
gigantea. Climbing to about 10 ft (3 m), with large inflated tubular flowers, bent in the middle to resemble a Dutch pipe (Dutchman's Pipe is the common name of a N. American species), and with a large lobe at the mouth. Purple. Brazil. Introduced by Lucombe, Pince & Co. in about 1846.

Arundinaria (Gramineae)
anceps. (syn: *A. jaunsarensis*) 'Pitt White'. A bamboo with canes to 1½ in. (4 cm) thick and 32 ft (10 m) high, sometimes growing 6 in. in 24 hours. Established at Dr Nathan Mutch's garden at Pitt White, Uplyme, it was obtained from Perry's Hardy Plant Farm at Enfield in 1940. Their stock was lost soon after, when nursery land was cleared for food production.

Asclepias (Asclepiadaceae) Milkweed
speciosa. The Butterfly Weed or Showy Milkweed. A softly-haired perennial, to 4½ ft (140 cm) high, with dense rounded heads of velvet buds and curious five-horned flowers, sweet smelling and soporific to insects, rose-purple and pinkish, from June to August. White woolly seed pods. Running underground. From Canada and west USA. One of the plants eaten by Monarch Butterfly caterpillars. First flowered at Lucombe, Pince & Co.'s Exeter nursery in 1846.
vestita. A Milkweed whose flowers are purple in bud, opening to greenish-white, in dense heads. Raised by Veitch from seeds sent from North America, which flowered for the first time in 1843.

Asplenium trichomanes 'Incisum Moule' (Aspleniaceae). See p.54

Aster (Compositae)
'Brixham Belle'. A vivid colour mixture of large fully double blooms produced on strong stems about 3 ft (1 m) high. Plants are vigorous, branch low down, and make an ideal subject for cutting as well as for a fine garden display. Annual. Raised by Sutton Seeds Ltd of Torquay in 1988.

'Devon Riviera'. Another race of double-flowered asters in a range of colours from late summer into autumn. About 2 ft (60 cm) tall. Annual. Raised by Suttons Seeds Ltd in the 1980s.
lateriflorus 'Coombe Fishacre'. Horizontal branches with tiny leaves, coppery purple by September, and little palest lilac-pink michaelmas-daisy flowers with rosy-brown centres. To 4 ft (120 cm) high. Raised by T.H. Archer Hind in about 1910 and named after his home near Ipplepen.
novi-belgii 'Davey's True Blue'. This michaelmas-daisy is 4 ft (120 cm) high with semi-double violet-blue flowers and was raised by V.G. Davey of Paignton.

Athyrium filix-femina 'Clarissima Jones' (Athyriaceae). See p54.

Atropa biflora (Solanaceae). See *Hebecladus biflorus*.

Aubrieta (Cruciferae)
'Mrs L.K. Elmhirst'. Clear pink flowers. 3 in. (7.5 cm) high. A variety selected at Dartington Hall in the 1930s.

Azara (Flacourtiaceae)
microphylla. A small tree with tiny polished evergreen leaves and small fluffy yellow flowers. vanilla-scented, in late winter and early spring. The only generally hardy Azara. Introduced from South America in about 1861 by Pearce collecting for Veitch of Exeter. FCC 1872.

Barbacenia (Velloziaceae)
squamata. Yucca-like leaves with toothed edges, to 6 in. (15 cm) long. Fragrant funnel-shaped flowers with spreading

petals, bright orange or scarlet. Moist warm greenhouse. William Lobb introduced this to Veitch in 1841, from the Organ Mountains of Brazil.

Befaria (Ericaceae). Densely leaved evergreen shrubs needing lime-free soil and a greenhouse. Rare in cultivation. The following were introduced from Peru by William Lobb for Veitch.

aestuans. To 15 ft (5 m) with rose-coloured flowers, the young leaves with rust-coloured hairs. 1846.

cinnamomea. Dense heads of purple flowers. 4 ft (120 cm). 1847.

coarctica. To 5 ft (1.5 m). Pale rose-pink flowers, streaked darker, in dense heads at the ends of shoots. 1847.

glauca tomentella. To 6 ft (2 m) with branches reddish haired and the flowers sulphur-yellow. 1844.

Begonia (Begoniaceae)

coccinea. The Angel-wing Begonia has red leaves and hanging coral-red flowers most of the year. To 6 ft (2 m) or so, with bamboo-like stems. A parent of many fibrous-rooted cultivars. Greenhouse.

PLATE 118
Begonia coccinea at University of Bristol Botanic Gardens

Introduced from Brazil in 1841 by William Lobb for Veitch.

pearcei. Velvety leaves with light red undersides. Large yellow flowers in the summer. A parent of many modern tuberous begonias, including those with yellow, buff and orange flowers. Greenhouse. Collected in Bolivia in 1865 by, and named after, the Devonian Richard Pearce for Veitch of Chelsea.

semperflorens 'Devon Gems'. About 6 in. (15 cm) high with pink to red or white flowers and green to chocolate-brown leaves. Raised by Suttons Seeds Ltd of Torquay, in the 1980s.

Beloperone (Acanthaceae)

guttata 'George Davey'. A seedling 'Shrimp Plant' raised by V. George Davey of Galmpton, Brixham, selected for its compact habit, being only about 1 ft (30 cm) tall. White flowers spotted red-purple, in yellow-green bracts that age red. Cool greenhouse. AM 1970.

Berberidopsis corallina (Flacourtiaceae). See p.31.

Berberis (Berberidaceae)

'Bickham Devonshire Cream'. A sport of × *stenophylla* with narrow evergreen leaves and cream flowers, that arose at Bickham House near Yelverton, recently.

darwinii. See p.32.

hakeoides (syn: *B. congestiflora hakeoides*). An evergreen shrub with rounded spiny leaves, many deep yellow flowers and a gaunt aspect. Discovered and introduced from Chile in 1862 by Richard Pearce working for Veitch of Exeter. AM 1901.

'Nitens'. Holly-like leaves, rich bronze emerging, ageing polished green. Dwarf and compact. Raised at Lucombe, Pince & Co.'s Exeter nursery in the last century and probably extinct.

thunbergii 'Marten's Pincushion'. A dwarf raised recently at Marten's Nurseries, Exeter.

Betula (Betulaceae) Birch
'Conyngham'. A seedling of *Betula albo-sinensis septentrionalis*, possibly crossed with the 'Silver Birch' (*B. pendula*). It has pinkish bark with a beautiful white bloom, and a pronounced weeping habit. Raised by Kenneth Ashburner of Stone Lane Gardens, Chagford.
ermanii 'Gold'. Raised by Kenneth Ashburner from seed sent from Hokkaido, Japan, and selected for the golden colour of the young branches.
pubescens 'Arnold Brembo'. See p.32.
utilis 'Kyelang'. See p.32.

Blechnum spicant (Blechnaceae)
'Biceps'. See p.56.
'Padleyense'. See p.56.

Bomarea (Alstroemeriaceae). Mostly climbing, with Alstroemeria-like flowers in summer and early autumn. Greenhouse, or perhaps outside against a wall in favoured gardens.
andimarcana. Tubular flowers to 2 in. (5 cm) long, the three outer petals orange tipped black and the three inner yellow-green. Seed was sent from the Andimarca Mountains in the Peruvian Andes by William Lobb to Veitch, who first flowered it in 1846.
caldasii. A twining climber with flowers of orange-yellow, tipped green, and the inner petals spotted crimson. Introduced from Ecuador in 1862, by Pearce for Veitch of Exeter.

PLATE 119
Bomarea caldasii

Brachysema (Leguminosae)
lanceolatum. The Swan River Pea-bush,

with silky branches and silvery buds, grows to about 4 ft (120 cm) high. Many rich scarlet flowers about 1 in. (2.5 cm) long, the upper petal edged white. Introduced from Western Australia by Lucombe, Pince & Co. in 1848.

Browallia jamesonii (Solanaceae)
See *Streptosolen.*

Brunnera (Boraginaceae)
macrophylla 'Langtrees'. Sprays of tiny vivid blue forget-me-not flowers in the spring and large rounded leaves, which in this cultivar have silvery spots near the edges. Moist soil and some shade. Raised by Dr A. Rogerson and named after his garden.

Buddleja (Loganiaceae)
davidii. 'Dartmoor'. See p.33.
Seedlings raised at Southcombe Gardens, Widecombe-in-the-Moor about 1975:
'Southcombe Blue'. Light violet-blue flowers, one of the bluest Buddlejas.
'Southcombe Splendour'. Large very dense flower spike with small spikes protruding from it. Light violet flowers.

Bulbophyllum (Orchidaceae). Tropical orchids growing on trees. Warm greenhouse. The following were introduced by Thomas Lobb to Veitch:
beccari. The largest-leaved orchid, climbing vigorously, with small flowers in autumn; light brown, clouded with violet, in dense pendulous spikes. Their stench is unbearable. Borneo 1853.
lobbii. Solitary buff-yellow flowers to 4 in. (10 cm) across, the tops spotted purple-red, and with deep yellow lips, in May-June and November. Java 1845.
reticulatum. White flowers, striped purple inside; yellow lip, spotted purple. Borneo 1852.

Burtonia (Leguminosae). Shrubs to about 2 ft (60 cm) high, often heather-like, with pea-flowers, needing rather dry treatment in a greenhouse. Raised by Lucombe, Pince & Co., from seed sent by James Drummond from the Swan River area of S.W. Australia.

brunoides. Woolly needle leaves. Yellow flowers. About 1845.

conferta. Violet flowers in July. 1830.

scabra (syn. *B. pulchella*). ¾ in. (2 cm) mauve-pink flowers in April. 1845.

villosa. Large purple flowers. 1846.

Calandrinia (Portulacaceae)

umbellata. Half-hardy perennial, sometimes treated as an annual or biennial. A *Lewisia* relative 4–6 in. (10–15 cm) high with fleshy leaves and dazzling magenta-crimson flowers, ¾ in. (2 cm) across, in heads, in July and August. Introduced from the Peruvian Andes by William Lobb for Veitch in 1846.

Calanthe (Orchidaceae). Greenhouse orchids:

'Dominii'. The first orchid hybrid ever raised, in 1853, by John Dominy at the Exeter Veitch's by crossing *C. masuca* with *C. furcata*. First flowered in 1856.

rosea. Pale rose flowers, shading to the white lip, in winter. Introduced for Veitch by Thomas Lobb in 1853 from Moulmein in Burma.

'Veitchii'. Flowers pink. Raised by John Dominy at the Veitch nursery Exeter. 1856.

vestita. Many pure white flowers in nodding spikes to 3 ft (1 m) long in winter. Introduced from Burma in 1848 by Dr Kane of Exmouth who sent two plants to Veitch of Exeter.

Calceolaria (Scrophulariaceae) Slipperwort Herbaceous or shrubby plants with leaves usually hairy and wrinkled. Flowers 2-lipped, the lower inflated and pouch-like.

alba. A narrow-leaved, rosemary-scented sticky sub-shrub to 2 ft (60 cm) tall with loose heads of nearly globular white

flowers in June. Greenhouse. Seed was sent from Chile in 1844 by William Lobb to Veitch.

amplexicaulis. Heads of pale yellow flowers in May and June. to 2½ ft (75 cm) high with a woody base and leaves clasping the stems. Half-hardy. Introduced from Peru in 1849 by William Lobb for Veitch.

crenata. Deep yellow flowers with almost no mouths, in open heads in the summer. 2½ ft+ (75 cm) tall. Greenhouse. Wild in Peru and Colombia; introduced in 1843 by William Lobb for Veitch of Exeter.

deflexa. A sub-shrub to 2 ft (60 cm) tall with heads of ¾ in. (2 cm) yellow flowers, with nearly equal-sized lips, in winter and spring. Greenhouse. Introduced by William Lobb to Veitch from Peru in 1849.

ericoides. Herbaceous plant, similar to a heather in habit and foliage. Abundant bright yellow flowers. Collected in Ecuador by Pearce for Veitch of Exeter in about 1860.

'Exoniensis'. A seedling shown by Lucombe, Pince & Co. at the 1834 Spring Show of the Devon and Exeter Botanical and Horticultural Society.

flexuosa. More or less shrubby, to 2½ ft (75 cm) tall, with yellow flowers nearly 1 in. (2.5 cm) across in large clusters. Collected in Peru in 1847 by William Lobb for Veitch.

pisacomensis. Yellowish-red or orange flowers, yellow under the large pouched bottom lip, on 18 in. (45 cm) stems. Greenhouse. Introduced from Ecuador (or perhaps Peru) by Pearce for Veitch of Exeter in about 1860.

tetragona. A compact shrub with shining leaves and pale yellow flowers with a rather square pouch. Greenhouse. Introduced from Peru by Veitch of Exeter before 1863.

'Veitchii'. 3 to 5 ft (1–1.5 m) tall with many small lemon-yellow flowers. Raised by Robert Veitch & Son before 1912 from *C. alba* crossed with an unknown cultivar.

Calluna (Ericaceae) Heather

vulgaris 'Mrs Ronald Gray'. A carpet a few inches high, with spikes of pale reddish-purple flowers in late summer. Found on a north Devon cliff by the late Dr Ronald Gray and introduced by Maxwell & Beale Ltd of Corfe Mullen, Dorset.

> 'Sampford Sunset'. A selected seedling of the heather 'Sunset' raised recently by Martin Hughes-Jones at Sampford Shrubs, Sampford Peverell. The foliage is orange and green-yellow, rather than the pink and orange of the parent.

Calyptridium umbellatum (Portulacaceae)
See *Spraguea umbellata*.

Camellia (Theaceae)

'Bernadice' has very pale red-purple flowers, semi-double, from April. Raised by K.M. White of Axminster about 1980.

'Carolyn Snowden'. See p.36.

japonica 'Devonia' ('Devoniensis'). Single or occasionally half-double white flowers with deep yellow stamens, bright green leaves and strong erect growths, raised by R. Veitch & Son of Exeter. AM 1900.

'Ma Belle'. Many small flowers, shell-pink and loosely double, on a spreading bush; raised by Dr J. Smart of Marwood.

'Mildred Veitch'. See p.36

'Wood Nymph'. A slightly pendulous bush with very early single to semi-double silver-pink flowers, with 10 instead of the more usual 8 petals of *C.* × *williamsii* camellias. Raised at The Garden House, Buckland Monachorum, before 1978.

Campanula (Campanulaceae)

persicifolia 'Pride of Exmouth'. Fat bell-flowers, semi-double (one inside another), rich lavender-blue, on 1½ ft (45 cm) stems, summer. Origin unknown; listed in a Dartington catalogue of about 1934.

Cantua (Polemoniaceae)

buxifolia. See p.36.

pyrifolia. An evergreen shrub or small tree with yellow trumpet-flowers, the 5-split mouth white, in dense heads in March. From Ecuador, Peru and Bolivia, sent to Veitch by William Lobb in 1848. Greenhouse.

Carex (Cyperaceae)

elata (syn: *C. stricta*) 'Knightshayes'. A clump-forming yellow sedge, a sport of Bowles' Golden Sedge with no green edges to the leaves, found at Knightshayes. Moist soil.

Cattleya (Orchidaceae)

aclandiae. See p.80.

Hybrids raised by John Dominy (1816-91). He was born at Gittisham and raised many orchid hybrids, working for Veitch of Exeter from about 1854 until 1864, when he joined the Chelsea firm. He is buried at Exeter.

> 'Devoniensis' ('Devonia'). Narrow white petals, deep purple lip. FCC 1864.
> 'Exoniensis' (× *Laeliocattleya* 'Exoniensis'). Pale blush flowers, lower lip marked deep rosy purple.
> 'Dominiana'.
> 'Hybrida'.

Ceanothus (Rhamnaceae). The following were sent to Veitch by William Lobb from California:

dentatus floribundus. Evergreen, 4–6 ft (125–200 cm) high, with rich blue flowers in May. The seed collected by Lobb produced plants with particularly vivid blue flowers, which may not now be in cultivation. 1848.
'Lobbianus'. Bright blue flowers on downy blue stalks in May and June. Large evergreen shrub. A natural hybrid, probably of *C. griseus* with *C. dentatus*, from Monterey. 1853. AGM 1969.
papillosus. See p.37.
sanguineus. Unlike many, the Red-

stemmed Ceanothus, or Oregon Tea, sheds its leaves in the autumn and has white flowers. 1853.

'Veitchianus'. See p.37.

velutinus. Dull white flowers in heads to 5 in. (12 cm) long, June and July. Large polished evergreen leaves, sticky and scented of resin in hot weather. To 10 ft (3 m). Plants from the original introduction were probably tender; those growing in the mountains of Oregon and Washington might be tougher. 1853.

Cedrus (Pinaceae)
libani brevifolia 'Kenwith'. This, the only known dwarf form of the Cyprus Cedar, forms a squat conical bush. Raised at Kenwith Castle Nurseries.

Centradenia (Melastomataceae)
inaequilateralis. A 1 ft (30 cm) high evergreen undershrub with the leaves reddish underneath, and showy 4-petalled pink flowers; needing light acid soil and a warm greenhouse. Introduced from Mexico in 1840 by Lucombe, Pince & Co.

PLATE 120
Chaenomeles speciosa 'Rosemoor' at Rosemoor Garden, Great Torrington

Centropogon (Campanulaceae)
coccineus. A woody-based plant about 3 ft (1 m) high with hanging tubular flowers about 2 in. (5 cm) long, intense crimson-scarlet. Warm greenhouse. Collected in the Organ Mountains of Brazil by William Lobb for Veitch in 1844.

Ceratostema (Ericaceae)
longiflorum. A 3–4 ft (100-125 cm) evergreen greenhouse shrub with 1½ in. (3.5 cm) long tubular rich scarlet flowers in summer, needing a moist acid soil. Introduced in 1846 from the Peruvian Andes by William Lobb for Veitch.

Ceropegia (Asclepiadaceae)
cumingiana. A twining climber with flowers of a peculiar shape, banded white, red, chocolate and yellow. Greenhouse. Introduced from Java by Thomas Lobb for Veitch, who first flowered it in 1847.

Chaenomeles (Rosaceae)
speciosa 'Rosemoor'. A flowering quince forming a spreading shrub with large scarlet-red spring flowers and fruits that make an excellent jelly. Raised at Rosemoor.

Chamaebatia (Rosaceae)
foliolosa. A rather delicate but attractive little semi-evergreen bush with ferny leaves, a balsam-like aroma and bramble-like flowers in June and July. Collected by William Lobb for Veitch in 1855 in California.

Chamaecyparis (Cupressaceae)
lawsoniana. Lawson's Cypress. 'Berrydown Gold' was introduced recently by Berrydown Nurseries, Gidleigh, who raised it from a seedling that was planted in about 1976 and is now about 9 ft (3 m) high; erect with yellow-gold foliage and somewhat drooping tips.

'Buckland Gold'. The original plant, raised in 1958 or before, is about 15 ft (5 m) high. Upright and neat with bright golden foliage. Raised at Champernowne's Green Lane Gardens near Yelverton.

M. Squires

PLATE 121
Chamaecyparis pisifera 'Devon Cream' at Chantry Nursery, Honiton

'Eclipse'. Growing to about 18 in. (45 cm) high and 12 in. (30 cm) wide in 10 years with blue-green and yellow foliage. Raised at Kenwith Castle Nurseries, Bideford, recently.

'Gold Pyramid'. About 2 ft (60 cm) high in 10 years, the plant has yellow foliage, soft to the touch. A sport of *C.l.* 'Chilworth Silver' at Kenwith Castle Nurseries.

'Snow White' is a slow-growing sport of *C.l.* 'Ellwoodii' with white-tipped new growths. It was raised by the wholesale Roberts Nurseries of East Allington and introduced by them in 1987.

'Sun King'. A slow-growing yellow bun with erect branches. A seedling of *C.l.* 'Lutea' at Kenwith Castle Nurseries.

'White Gnome'. Very slow-growing bush, the white foliage having a few green sprays. A sport on a plant of *C.l.* 'Gnome' at Kenwith Castle Nurseries.

Introduced or raised by Don Hatch, Chantry Nursery, Coombe Raleigh, Honiton. For 25 years Don Hatch ran a retail alpine and dwarf conifer nursery at Farnham in Surrey. In 1973 he and his wife moved to Devon for semi-

retirement, but such was the demand for their dwarf conifers that they established a full-time wholesale nursery, overcoming difficulties which included a flash flood that washed away plants to as far as Budleigh Salterton beach. Don died in 1986; the nursery has been continued by his widow, Gloria.

'Gnome'. A dense dark green mound. The original plant was 2 ft (60 cm) high and over 3 ft (90 cm) across when 15 years old.

'Little Spire.' A dark green spire dusted with scarlet male flowers in early summer, growing 6 ft (2 m) in 10 years. It was raised by crossing *C.l.* 'Fletcheri' with *C.l.* 'Wisselii'.

'Silver Threads'. A slow-growing column with silver-cream variegations, needing shelter from cold winds. A sport of *C.l.* 'Ellwood's Gold' at Kelvin Lawrence's Surrey nursery, introduced in 1981 by Chantry Nursery.

obtusa 'Erika'. A narrow bush, with prickly sage-green foliage, growing to about 2 ft (60 cm) in 10 years. A juvenile shoot on a plant of *C.o.* 'Nana Gracilis' at Chantry Nursery.

pisifera. Sawara Cypress
'Devon Cream'. The silver-blue foliage has creamy highlights. Slow-growing. A sport of *C.p.* 'Boulevard' raised at Chantry Nursery.

'Gold Cushion'. 2½ in. (6 cm) high and 8 in. (20 cm) wide after 10 years. Dark yellow foliage. A sport of *C.p.* 'Plumosa Aurea Nana' at Kenwith Castle Nurseries.

Cheiranthus (Cruciferae). See *Erysimum*.

Chirita (Gesneriaceae)
horsfieldii. A coarse stemless perennial up to 2 ft (60 cm) tall, with rough hairy evergreen leaves and flowers yellowish-white, tinged purple at the bases, tubular,

drooping and lipped. July. Greenhouse. Collected by Thomas Lobb in 1846 from Java for Veitch. The species has been confused with *C. lavandulacea.*

Chrysanthemum (Compositae). The florists' chrysanthemums 'Miss Mary Godfrey' and 'Pride of Exmouth' were raised at the W.J. Godfrey nursery in Exmouth in the early years of this century. They received an AM in 1925 for 'Gorgeous', an extra large dark crimson single.

frutescens 'Overbecks Gold'. See *Argyranthemum.*

Chysis (Orchidaceae)
aurea maculata. An orchid with tawny yellow flowers, marked purple, growing on trees in the wild. Greenhouse. Introduced from Venezuela in 1850 by Lucombe, Pince & Co.

Cineraria (Compositae)
'Wonder of the West', which included at least 35 forms, was raised by Lucombe, Pince & Co. in the 19th century. Cinerarias of gardens are selections and/or hybrids of *Senecio cruentus* from the Canary Islands.

Cissus cordifolius (syn: *C. porphyrophyllus*) (Vitaceae) See *Piper porphyrophyllum.*

Cistus 'Anne Palmer' (Cistaceae). See p.37.

Clematis (Ranunculaceae). Climbing unless otherwise noted.
'Hatherly'. A seedling of *C. tibetana vernayi* (*C. orientalis* of gardens), raised at the Hatherly Laboratories of Exeter University in the early 1960s. It is almost certainly a cross with *C. tangutica* and has lantern-shaped flowers with very thick orange-yellow petals.

montana grandiflora. *C. montana* is a white flowered species from the Himalayas. This form has larger flowers, up to 3¼ in. (8 cm) across.

Introduced by Veitch and first flowered outside in Exeter 1844.
smilacifolia (syn: *C. glandulosa*). A greenhouse species of Traveller's Joy. Dark purple, almost black petals, with a central mass of pure white anthers. Introduced by Veitch through Thomas Lobb from Mt Salak in Java, 1846.

Raised or introduced by Peveril Clematis Nursery:
alpina 'Jacqueline du Pré'. The outer parts of the flowers are shaded warm pink, the inner soft pink, edged silver-pink; April–May. 6–8 ft (200–250 cm).

'Chalcedony'. Large ice-blue double flowers in May–June and September. 8–12 ft (250–400 cm) with erect stems and leathery leaves.
integrifolia is a non-climbing Clematis, dying down in the winter, and growing to about 4 ft (120 cm) high. Peveril have raised:
'Pastel Blue' with powder blue flowers and
'Pastel Pink' with very pale pink flowers, both in July.

'James Mason'. Large single white ribbed flowers with maroon stamens in the centres, May–June and September. 8–12 ft (250–400 cm).

'John Huxtable'. See p.39.

'Kiri Te Kanawa'. Large very double blue flowers.

ladakhiana. Introduced from the Kashmir Himalaya. Similar to *C. tibetana vernayi* (*C. orientalis* of gardens) with small yellow flowers in August and September and ferny foliage. To 15 ft (5 m).
'Ladybird Johnson'. A cross between *C. texensis* and *C.* 'Bees Jubilee', the trumpet flowers being dusky red with cream-yellow stamens inside. Named in honour of Mrs Johnson's work for the Wild-flower Research Centre in Texas.

J. Lloyd

PLATE 122
Clematis 'Peveril Pearl' at Peveril Nursery, Christow

macropetala 'Snowbird'. Nodding white flowers, rather double, in April and May. 8–10 ft (250–300 cm).

montana 'Peveril'. Introduced from Sichuan in China. White flowers with widely spaced petals and extra-long stamens in the centre; second half of July.

'Mrs James Mason'. Double flowers in May and June, velvety red with wide violet-blue margins, and cream stamens. The September flowers are single with frilly edges. 8–12 ft (250–400 cm).

'Peveril Pearl'. Many large lustrous lilac flowers with pinky midribs, and cream stamens topped with violet anthers; May–June and September. 8–12 ft (250–400 cm).

recta 'Peveril'. *C. recta* is a floppy herbaceous plant. 'Peveril' stays erect, to 3 ft (1 m) high, with clouds of fragrant white flowers in June and July.

'The Princess of Wales'. See p.39.

viticella 'Elvan'. Nodding 2 in. (5 cm) flowers; the purple petals have white feathering; July to September. To 12 ft (4 m).

'Mary Rose'. See p.38.

Clerodendrum (Verbenaceae). (syn: *Clerodendron*.)

Shrubs or climbers. The flowers, in flat or domed clusters, have a slender tube with five petals at the mouth, from which the stamens stick out. The following are greenhouse species:

bethuneanum. A shrub to 10 ft (3 m) tall with heart-shaped leaves to 14 in. (40 cm) across. Crimson flowers in clusters to 5 in. (12 cm) across forming heads to 3 ft (1 m) long, in September. Introduced from Borneo by a Mr Lowe to Lucombe, Pince & Co., who first flowered it in 1850.

capitatum. A thorny shrub or small tree with large broad leaves and heads of heavily scented cream-white flowers with tubes to 4½ in. (11 cm) long. The hollow twigs are used for pipe stems, etc. Introduced by Thomas Whitfield to Lucombe, Pince & Co., in 1822 from Sierra Leone. Whitfield made several voyages to and journeys in West Africa collecting living plants and animals.

cruentum. Rich red flowers. Introduced from tropical Asia in 1860 by Thomas Lobb for Veitch.

macrophyllum. Java.

speciosissimum. Java Glorybean. Evergreen. To 5 ft (150 cm) high. Vivid scarlet flowers 2 in. (5 cm) across in large spreading heads. Introduced from Java, via Belgium, by Lucombe, Pince & Co. in 1835.

umbellatum (syn: *C. scandens)*. Climbing; white flowers tinged pink, dark centres, about 1 in. (2.5 cm) across. August to December. Tropical Africa.

Clianthus (Leguminosae)

formosus. (syn: *C. dampieri)* Sturt's Desert Pea, Glory Pea. A tender sprawler, with ferny blue-green leaves, and bunches of brilliant red flowers with a large purplish black central patch. A desert plant unhappy in the U.K.; it can be perpetuated for a while with difficulty if grafted as a young seedling on *Colutea arborescens.* Greenhouse. Introduced from Australia by Veitch who first flowered it in 1858.

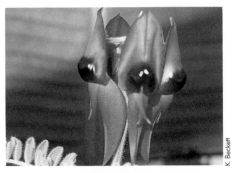

PLATE 123
Clianthus formosus

Clitoria (Leguminosae)
fulgens. A twining climber with glowing scarlet pea-flowers in June. Greenhouse. Found in rocky places in the Organ Mountains of Brazil. Introduced by Veitch c.1844.

Coelogyne (Orchidaceae). Fragrant evergreen orchids for the greenhouse, introduced by Thomas Lobb for Veitch:
lentiginosa. Straw-coloured to clear yellow flowers, the side pieces of the lip edged in brown, the larger mid piece white speckled with orange, in 4 or 5 in. (10–12 cm) long spikes. Summer. South Burma. 1847.
schilleriana (syn: *Pleione schilleriana*). Burma 1857.
speciosa. Flowers over 3 in. (7.5 cm) across, brownish or olive-green; yellow lip with dark red veins. Most of the year. Java and Sumatra. 1845.

Collinsia (Scrophulariaceae). Leafy erect annuals with split-lipped 'snapdragon' flowers. The following were introduced from California by William Lobb for Veitch in 1852:
bartsiaefolia. Pale lilac flowers. 6–9 in. (15-23 cm) high.
bicolor multicolor. Flowers white, with lilac, rose or violet stripes or markings. 1½ ft (45 cm) high.

Cordia (Boraginaceae)
decandra. A 3 ft (1 m) greenhouse shrub with fragrant white trumpet flowers in May. William Lobb sent seed from Chile, which was received by Veitch of Exeter in 1849. Plants were raised but did not flower until 1875.

Cordyline (Agavaceae)
australis. Cultivars of the Torbay Palm, or New Zealand Cabbage tree, raised recently at the Torbay Palm Farm, Coffinswell, include:
'Torbay Dazzler'. Green leaves with cream-yellow edges and, especially on the undersides, red midribs.
'Torbay Red'. Deep wine red leaves (1980).
'Torbay Sunset'. Green leaves with red midribs.
'Torbay Surprise'. Green leaves lined light yellow.

Cornus nuttallii 'Portlemouth' (Cornaceae) See p.39.

Coronilla (Leguminosae)
glauca 'Citrina'. An evergreen shrub with fragrant pale lemon yellow flowers in April, sometimes earlier, and intermittently through the summer. Blue-green leaves. Needs sun and mild winters; it is less hardy than the species. Selected by Roy Cheek of Cannington from a plant in Dr Barker's garden at East Portlemouth, opposite Salcombe, in the 1970s.

Cotoneaster (Rosaceae)
wilsonii. A shrub about 5 ft (1.5 m) high with heads of white flowers and bunches of reddish-purple berries. Introduced to (and first flowered at) Rosemoor from Ullung Do Island, east of Korea, by John Gallagher, recently.

Crawfurdia fasciculata (Gentianaceae) See *Gentiana fascicularis.*

Crinodendron hookerianum
(Elaeocarpaceae). See p.40.

Cryptomeria (Taxodiaceae)
japonica Lobbii. Thomas Lobb sent seed
of this form of Japanese Cedar to Veitch in
1853, from the Buitenzorg Botanic
Garden in Java, to which it had been
introduced by Siebold in the 1820s. The
foliage is in dense bunches, giving the tree
a very irregular outline. At Endsleigh a
specimen had reached 118 ft (36 m) in
1970.

Cuphea (Lythraceae)
cordata. Related to the familiar Cigar
Flower, *C. ignea*, this is an
18 in. (45 cm) tall evergreen, sticky, tender
undershrub with scarlet tubular flowers in
June, easily grown in ordinary soil in a
greenhouse. Introduced by William Lobb
for Veitch from Peru in 1842.

Cupressus (Cupressaceae)
macnabiana. The MacNab Cypress is a
bushy tree to about 30 ft (9 m) high with
dark grey-green foliage, aromatic when
bruised; probably short-lived in this
country. Introduced from the Californian
Sierra Nevada in 1854 by both William
Lobb for Veitch and W. Murray for
Lawson of Edinburgh.
macrocarpa 'Sulphur Tip'. A dwarf
Monterey Cypress growing a little over
2 ft (60 cm) high, spreading, with pale
yellow tips all year, though more so in
summer. Introduced by Chantry Nursery.

Cycnoches (Orchidaceae)
pentadactylon. The Swan Orchid grows
on trees in Brazil. The flower, nearly 4 in.
(10 cm) across, has a green outside slightly
touched with reddish brown, yellow inside,
blotched and striped chocolate crimson-
red, and its lip divided into five fingers.
Greenhouse. The first to flower at Exeter,
in 1842, of the orchids collected by
William Lobb.

Cymbidium (Orchidaceae). Greenhouse
orchids.
Bo-peep 'Combe Hill' was raised by R.H.
Palmer of Newton Abbot. A miniature
orchid with buff flowers lined and flushed
rose purple; the lips white, blotched
crimson. A.M. 1962.
grandiflorum. Flowers to 5 in. (12 cm)
across, green; lip straw-coloured with deep
yellow edges surrounded by purple-red
blotches, in arching spikes. Sikkim,
Himalaya. Introduced by Thomas Lobb
for Veitch of Exeter, but it did not flower
until 1866 at Chelsea.

Cypripedium (Orchidaceae) Lady's Slipper
Orchid.
barbatum. See *Paphiopedilum barbatum.*
caudatum. The flowers' top sepals are 5 or
6 in. (12–15 cm) long, cream-white tinged
and veined with green; the hanging
ribbon-like petals may be 2½ ft (75 cm)
long, reddish-brown with yellowish-green
bases; the swollen lip is also reddish-
brown, the same colour as spots on its
yellow base. April and May. Greenhouse.
Introduced by William Lobb for Veitch
from Peru in 1851. Sometimes included in
Phragmipedilum.
javanicum. See *Paphiopedilum javanicum*
villosum. See *Paphiopedilum villosum.*

Daboecia (Ericaceae).
cantabrica 'Covadonga'. A form of the
large-flowered St Dabeoc's Heath where
the usually egg-shaped bloom is split into a
crimson-purple star. Introduced by Terry
Underhill from the Picos Mountains in
North Spain in 1973.

Dahlia (Compositae)
'Ashtor'. Small globe flowers, sulphur
yellow tipped red. 4 ft (120 cm) high.
Raised by M.D. Jones at the now closed
Bickington Nurseries, near Newton
Abbot, before 1966.

A. Kingdon

PLATE 124
Daphne 'G. K. Argles' at Cottage Garden Nursery

'Deanna Kerkrade'. Small yellow "cactus" flowers. Raised recently by Harry W. Hooper of Broadfields, Exeter.

'Pink Kerkrade'. Small cactus flowers, dark pink with cream centres; a sport of 'Majestic Kerkrade' raised in 1982 by H.W. Hooper. Many awards at Dahlia shows and trials.

'Reginald Godfrey'. Raised at the W.J. Godfrey nursery in Exmouth about 1925.

'Rose Preference'. 5 in. (12 cm) cactus flowers, primrose-yellow shaded with rose pink, the inner parts with a gold sheen. 4 ft (120 cm) high. Raised before 1965 by M.D. Jones.

'Selway Darrell'. 5½ in. (14 cm) red flowers, the interior touched with yellow. Nearly 5 ft (1.5 m) high. Raised before 1967 by R.D. Stevens, Selway Lodge, Looseleigh Cross, Plymouth. He also raised 'Selway Karen' and 'Selway Mary'.

'Sue Willo'. A sport of 'Willo's Violet', with small pompom flowers, white with purple tips, purple from a distance. 4½ ft (140 cm) high. It has received many awards at Dahlia shows. Raised by Dennis J. Cole of West Alvington, near Kingsbridge, named after his daughter, and introduced in 1966.

Daphne (Thymelaceae)

'G.K. Argles'. *D. × burkwoodii* is a partly evergreen shrub 2 to 4 ft (60–120 cm) high with clusters of sweetly scented white flowers, ageing pale pink, in May and June. 'G.K. Argles', with a very good gold variegation on the leaves, was a sport on a plant at the Argles' wholesale nursery, E.B. Champernowne at Buckland Monachorum, selected by Colin Carver, then a propagator there, now running his own nursery.

odora 'Baker's Gold'. See p.41.

Davallia (Polypodiaceae). Tropical ferns with much divided fronds; Thomas Lobb, collecting for Veitch of Exeter, introduced the following from Borneo, or nearby:

affinis.

alpina (syn: *Humata alpina*). Creeping, with fronds to 3 in. (7.5 cm) long.

pallida (syn: *Leucostegia pallida*). A fast-growing plant with 2–3 ft (60–90 cm) fronds.

parvula (syn: *Humata parvula*). Creeping widely, with fronds about ¾ x ½ in. (2 x 1 cm).

H. Hooper

PLATE 125
Dahlia 'Pink Kerkrade'

Delphinium (Ranunculaceae)
cardinale. The Scarlet Larkspur has bright luminous red flowers in open spires on 3 to 6 ft (1–2 m) stems in the summer, the plant dying down soon after. Half-hardy and probably short-lived, it can be flowered from seed sown early in the same year. Native to dry openings in thickets and woods in S.W. California. Discovered by William Lobb in about 1850 and sent to Veitch.

Dendrobium (Orchidaceae). Orchids for a warm greenhouse, introduced by Thomas Lobb for Veitch:
albosanguineum. 4 in. (10 cm) cream-white flowers with a little blood-red streaking near the centres; the lip has one or two large patches of crimson. June. Burma 1851.

amoenum (syn: *D. mesochlorum*). White flowers with small violet-purple tips and yellow throats; violet-scented. Summer. Himalaya 1843.

cretaceum. Small chalky white flowers, the lip with a pale yellow mark crossed by fine crimson lines. May. India 1846.

macrophyllum (syn: *D. veitchianum*). A variable plant with 2 in. (5 cm) cream to greenish flowers with black bristles on the outsides, the three-part waxy lip striped and spotted purple. Summer. Philippines.

palpebrae. White flowers, the base of the lip with an orange-yellow circular patch and 5 lines of reddish hairs, on stems to 9 in. (23 cm). Late summer. Borneo. 1849.

tortile. 3in. (7.5 cm) very pale yellow flowers clouded purple-pink. June. Burma 1847.

transparens. See-through white flowers, light purplish-rose tips, the lip with a yellow-edged deep crimson stain. March. Assam. 1852.

xanthophlebium. White flowers, sides of the lip veined orange, the middle orange-yellow edged in white. Burma.

Dendromecon rigida (Papaveraceae). See p.44.

Desfontainea spinosa (Potaliaceae). See p.44.

Dianthus (Caryophyllaceae) Pinks. See also p.45.
Raised by Harold Bawden, and named after his garden at Offwell near Honiton:
'Weetwood Double': fragrant double pink flowers on 6 to 9 in. (15–23 cm) stems from June to August.
Raised by R. Bloomfield of Dawlish:
'Pink Monica Wyatt': a sport of 'Monica Wyatt' in 1987.
Raised by David Bowen of Dawlish:
'Jane Bowen'. A very fragrant claret-coloured sport of 'Bovey Belle'.
Raised by E.A. (Nellie) Britton at Washfield Nursery near Tiverton:
'Craddock Pink': a seedling of 'Highland Fraser' with small double pink flowers.
Raised at Dartington Hall:
'Dartington Double': small double red flowers.
Raised at the W.J. Godfrey nursery in Exmouth:
'Reginald Godfrey': salmon-pink perpetual carnation (introduced 1896).
'Exmouth Gem'.
'Queen of the Exe'.
Raised by Ray Hubbard at Hill House, Landscove:
'Buckfast Abbey': fragrant dark lavender-mauve flowers. 1987.
'Little Miss Muffet': pink, flushed deeper pink at edges. 1987.
'Old Mother Hubbard': a sport of 'Doris'. Pale pink flowers with carmine-rose stripes. 1985. AM 1988.

Raised at Southcombe Gardens, Widecombe-in-the-Moor (selected for the combination of ornament and tolerance of winter wet):

'Amarinth': fragrant deep pink with maroon pentangle round centre.

'Besarion': deep velvety red-purple spotted and edged lighter.

'Hakem': frilly-edged white.

'Hermanric': large very pale pink, frilled edges, velvet red pentangle round centre.

'Orchan': fragrant red-purple flowers above low greyish mats.

'Tarif': purple-red, velvety ring round centre.

'Tribigild': velvety magenta-purple, light edges.

Raised by H.R. Whetman & Son, Houndspool, Dawlish:

'Devon Blush': rose-pink with a carmine ring (1988).

'Devon Cream': chrome-yellow with a magenta flush (1987).

'Devon Flame': mandarin red (1988).

'Devon Glow': red-purple; strong clove scent (1988).

'Houndspool Cheryl': fragrant ruby-red sport of 'Houndspool Ruby' (1980). AM 1986.

'Houndspool Ruby': purple-pink with a ruby red ring; sport of 'Doris' (1978).

Raised by Cecil Wyatt, Colehayes, Bovey Tracey:

'Anna Wyatt': double carmine-rose, strong scent. (1978). AM 1982.

'Becka Falls': double signal-red. (1980). AM 1982.

'Bovey Belle': double dark magenta, strong clove scent. (1979). AM 1984.

'Clea Wyatt': pink.

'Colehayes Crimson'.

'Cranmere Pool': cream-white, dark magenta centre, double. (1984). FCC 1987.

'Dartmoor Forest': crimson, clove scented. (1978). AM 1982.

'Green Lanes': white.

'Haytor': double pure white, fragrant (1971). AM 1982.

'Haytor Rock': scarlet streaks on pale pink, double (1980).

'Jenny Wyatt': pale shell pink, double (1985).

'Kestor': double light magenta, clove-scented; seedling of 'Haytor'. (1970). AM 1982.

'Letitia Wyatt': double blush pink, strongly scented. (1981). AM 1984.

'Monica Wyatt': pale purplish-pink, ruby-red centre, double, very fragrant; seedling of 'Valda Wyatt', more vigorous than its parent. (1984). AM 1984.

'Raspberry Ripple': pink flecked darker.

'Salmon Leap': double pink.

'Strawberries and Cream': pale pink, lined and flecked darker, large and double. (1984).

'Strawberry Fair': pink progeny of 'Strawberries and Cream'.

'Valda Wyatt': purplish-pink, darker centre, half-double, strongly scented. (1980). Named after his wife. AM 1982, FCC 1983.

'Widecombe Fair': pale salmon-pink, double; scented. (1979).

Border carnations raised in the 1890s by H. Hammond Spencer, gardener to G. Foster at Glendavagh, Teignmouth:

'Cecil': large scarlet flowers.

'Cycle': bright yellow flowers, slightly purplish, deep purple edges.

'Devonia': terra-cotta ground, with scarlet and purple flakes.

'Mrs G. Foster': large yellow flowers.

Dicentra (Papaveraceae)

chrysantha. Golden Ear-Drops. Feathery pale green foliage with a whitish bloom, deep yellow heart-shaped flowers in open clusters in the autumn. 2–6 ft (60–200 cm). Native to dry slopes, especially where burned or otherwise cleared, in California. Best in full sun and an infertile soil. Probably half-hardy. Introduced by William Lobb for Veitch in 1852.

formosa 'Langtrees'. See p.46.

Didymocarpus (Gesneriaceae)
crinitus. About 1 ft (30 cm) high, the leaves covered in red velvet, the trumpet-shaped flowers white tinged with purple. Sent from Singapore by Thomas Lobb to Veitch of Exeter, where it first flowered in their greenhouses in 1846.

Dimorphotheca (Compositae). See *Osteospermum.*

Dipladenia (Apocynaceae). Twiners, usually evergreen, for a well-drained border in the greenhouse, the wide flowers varying from trumpet- to nearly plate-shaped:
crassinoda. Climbing to about 10 ft (3 m) high, with flared trumpet flowers of a fine rose colour, with orange throats. Introduced by Lucombe, Pince & Co., who obtained seed from Brazil.
hirsuta (syn: *Mandevilla hispida* and *Echites hirsuta*). Sulphur yellow flowers, lined deep rose in the throat, 2½ in. (6 cm) across. Introduced for Veitch by William Lobb in 1842 from the Organ Mountains in Brazil.
splendens. Semi-evergreen. Growing from a tuber. 4 in. (10 cm) pinky-white funnel-shaped flowers with deeper-coloured throats, in spikes, opening one at a time. Introduced from the Organ Mountains of Brazil in 1841 by William Lobb for Veitch.
urophylla. Hanging heads of salmon-yellow flowers. About 3 ft (1 m) high. Introduced from Brazil in 1847 by William Lobb for Veitch.

Drimys (Winteraceae)
winteri 'Woodside'. A seedling of the broad-leaved form in the garden of Mervyn Feesey in Barnstaple. After over twenty-five years the plant is 30 ft 10 m) tall and only 10 ft (3 m) or less wide, making it a good fastigiate evergreen.

PLATE 126
Dipladenia splendens at Keeper's Cottage, Deancombe

Dryopteris (Aspidiaceae)
aemula 'Cristata'. See p.54.
dilatata 'Hymenophylloides'. See p.54.
filix-mas 'Polydactyla Dadds'. See p.54.

Echites hirsuta (Apocynaceae). See *Dipladenia hirsuta.*

Embothrium coccineum (Proteaceae) See p.47.

Endymion hispanicus 'Chevithorne' (Liliaceae). See *Hyacinthoides* p.59.

Erica (Ericaceae). Heather
arborea 'Picos Pigmy'. See p.47.
cinerea 'Heathfield'. This variety of the Bell Heather is up to 2½ ft (75 cm) high with many plum-coloured flowers. August-October. Found at Heathfield, Bovey Tracey by Neil Treseder.
  'Old Rose'. Low growing with pale rose flowers June-September. Found in Devon by Mr & Mrs J.F. Letts, of heather nursery fame, before 1964.
tetralix 'Melbury White'. A Cross-leaved Heath found on Melbury Common. Slow-growing, compact and grey-foliaged, with white flowers in large heads.

× *veitchii* 'Exeter'. Growing to 6 ft (2 m) tall it has bright green foliage and masses of fragrant white flowers in the spring. Not for cold areas. A chance seedling at Veitch's Exeter nursery before 1900, a cross betwen *E. arborea* and *E. lusitanica*. A.M. 1905.

ventricosa 'Wellsiana'. A variety of this Cape Heath shown among 21 others by Lucombe, Pince & Co. in 1843, and named after Mrs Wells of Cowley House, near Exeter, who had an extensive collection of orchids and Cape Heaths.

Erigeron (Compositae)
'Four Winds'. Similar to *Erigeron glaucus*; forming evergreen clumps about 1 ft (30 cm) high with bright purplish-red flowers from July. It needs a sunny spot, dryish in winter. Raised at Four Winds Nursery, Georgeham (run by Commander Laurence Phillips) flourished 1950s.

Erysimum (Cruciferae). Perennial wallflowers. The first two of the plants below were found in the garden of Mrs Ludovic Amory at Chevithorne:

'Aunt May'. Flat growing, with small fine leaves. Multicoloured flowers.

'Chevithorne'. Upright with golden-yellow, double flowers. 2½ ft (75 cm).

'L.K. Elmhirst'. See p.48.

Erythronium revolutum 'Knightshayes Pink' (Liliaceae). See p.49.

Escallonia (Escalloniaceae)
× *exoniensis*. See p.52.
laevis (syn: *E. organensis*). An evergreen bush with late rose-red flowers, of dubious hardiness, introduced from Brazilian mountain ravines in 1844 by William Lobb for the Exeter firm of Veitch.
rosea (syn: *E. pterocladon*). Small narrow evergreen leaves; fragrant white flowers in July and August, 6 ft (2 m) high or more, often hardy. Introduced from Chile in

1847 by William Lobb for Veitch of Exeter.
rubra macrantha (syn: *E. macrantha*). See p.52.
virgata. An *Escallonia* unusual in having white wide-open flowers, leaves falling off in the autumn, and general hardiness. Introduced by Pearce from his 1859–62 visit to Chile, for Veitch of Exeter. FCC 1888.

Eschscholzia (Papaveraceae)
caespitosa. The Tufted Poppy has feathery pale blue-green leaves and many stems 4 to 16 in. (10–40 cm) tall, bearing bright yellow flowers. An annual for a sunny dryish spot. Introduced from California in about 1850 by William Lobb for Veitch.

Eucalyptus (Myrtaceae)
pauciflora pendula. A weeping form of the 'Cabbage Gum' with a silver-grey trunk; grey leaves, long, narrow and curved; and white flowers in June. Introduced recently by Dr J. Smart of Marwood from seed he collected in the Snowy Mountains of New South Wales.

PLATE 127
Eucalyptus pauciflora pendula at Woodside, near Barnstaple

Eucryphia glutinosa (Eucryphiaceae)
See p.53.

Euodia (Rutaceae)
baberi. Growing to 50 ft (15 m) high in the wild, it has handsome pungent-scented ash-like leaves, dark purple young shoots, large heads of small whitish flowers and reddish berries. Seed of this tree was collected by Roy Lancaster (under collectors number L594) on Mount Omei in China in 1980, from which, at Rosemoor, was raised the only plant known in the U.K.

Euphorbia (Euphorbiaceae) Spurge
characias 'Benger's Silver'. See p.53.
epithymoides (syn: *E. polychroma*) 'Victor's Purple'. The type forms clumps about 16 in. (40 cm) high, with, on the form usually grown, bright metallic yellow flower cups. 'Victor's Purple' has purple new growths, purplish-green foliage and flower cups of a darker yellow. A seedling selected recently by S. Pawlowski at Buckland Monachorum.

PLATE 128
Fremontodendron californica at Lustleigh

Eurygania (Ericaceae)
ovata. Evergreen bush with drooping branches and white-mouthed red flowers in fat bunches 4–5 in. (10-12 cm) wide. Greenhouse conditions with acid, light, fibrous and sandy soil. Introduced from the Andes of Peru by William Lobb for Veitch.

Fitzroya (Cupressaceae)
cupressoides (syn: *F. patagonica*). A cypress-like tree with drooping foliage introduced in 1849 to Veitch of Exeter by William Lobb from a rainy part of Chile. The largest tree in the UK is at Killerton; it was 60ft (18 m) high when 106 years old.

Fragaria (Rosaceae) Strawberry

'Bicton Pine'. It had large yellowish-white fruit, tinged red on the sunny side, and white flesh. Raised before 1847 by James Barnes, Head Gardener to Lady Rolle at Bicton. He complained that Lady Rolle exchanged the stock of this strawberry for plants for her park from Knight & Perry at Chelsea.

'Miller's Ruby'. Raised at Harpford, next to Newton Poppleford, and introduced by George Pyne, Denver Nurseries, Topsham.
vesca var. *fructu hispida*. Plymouth Strawberry. See p.57.

Francoa (Saxifragaceae)
sonchifolia 'Rogerson'. A seedling of the Bridal Wreath raised and selected by Tony Rogerson at Langtrees in about 1970. It has deep pink flowers on 18 in. (45 cm) stems, above clumps of lobed leaves. Not for cold areas.

Fremontodendron (Sterculiaceae)
californicum. Large yellow flowers all summer on a tall shrub, if grown against a

wall in a dryish sunny spot with lenient winters. It was first introduced to the Horticultural Society's garden at Chiswick in about 1850 as a single plant that refused to be propagated. In 1859 the Society was in financial difficulties and the plant was sold to Henderson's nursery but did not long survive the move and had no progeny. Meanwhile Veitch of Exeter had more successfully introduced it from a collection by William Lobb in 1853. FCC 1866.

PLATE 129
Fuchsia 'Whirlybird' at Elburton, Plymouth

Fuchsia (Onagraceae)
    denticulata (syn: *F. serratifolia*). Cloud forest of Peru and Bolivia. A tender shrub up to 12 ft (4 m) tall with glossy green foliage and 2 in. (5 cm) long flowers with crimson-red tube, green-tipped sepals and vermilion petals. Introduced by William Lobb to Veitch in 1845, flowered 1846.
    macrantha (syn: *F. apetala*). Upper cloud forest of Peru and Bolivia. A tender, prostrate or climbing shrub, often growing on trees, with pink petal-less flowers up to 6 in. (15 cm) long, crowded at the ends of short side shoots. Introduced by William Lobb to Veitch in 1845, flowered in 1846.

macrostigma (syn: *F. spectabilis*). Cloud forest of Ecuador and Colombia. A tender shrub up to 5 ft (1.5 m) tall with velvety dark green leaves, purple below, and horizontal red flowers 3 in. (7.5 cm) long. Introduced by William Lobb to Veitch in 1848.

magellanica 'Sharpitor'. See p.59.

simplicicaulis. Bright purplish-red flowers to 3 in. (7.5 cm) long. A plant was formerly trained high in the roof of a temperate house at Kew Gardens. Introduced from Peru by William Lobb to Veitch.

Bred by George Hilton, Plymouth:
  1976 'Jennifer Hampson' (Seedling of 'Dollar Princess'): trailing; double; cerise and purple.
      'Debra Hampson' (sport of 'Dark Eyes'): double; red and mauve.
      'Mrs Hilton' ('Prelude' × 'Swingtime'): semi-double; white and lilac.
      'Kim Hampson' ('Swingtime' × 'Prelude'): semi-double; pink and violet.

  1978 'Dartmoor Pixie': single; red and purple.
      'Mount Edgecumbe': single; white and red.
      'Plymouth Hoe': semi-double; pale pink and deeper pink with some purple.
      'Plymouth Sound': trailing; single; red and magenta.
      'The Classic'.

  1981 'Kingfisher': double; white and violet.
      'Drake Fourhundred': double; sepals twisted; red and purple.
      'Devonshire Dumpling': trailing; fat double flowers, white with pink sepals.
      'Whirlybird': single; white with pink sepals.

1984 'Debra' ('Mrs Hilton' × 'Merry Mary'): white and pale violet-purple.
'Drake's Drum' ('Whirlybird' × 'Bicentennial'): trailing; deep pink and violet-purple.
'Grandma' ('Drake Fourhundred' × 'Merry Mary'): double pink and violet.
'Lady Plymouth' ('Pink Galore' × 'Drake Fourhundred'): double; deeper and paler pink.
'Pastell' ('Drake Fourhundred' × 'Devonshire Dumpling'): double; pink and purple.
'Romany Rose' ('Mount Edgecumbe' × 'Merry Mary'): single; shades of pink.

Bred by Robert Pince of Lucombe, Pince & Co., Exeter:
'Earl of Devon'. Carmine, with the velvety reddish-purple petals forming a cup, said in an undated Lucombe, Pince & Co. catalogue to have been raised by Pince. It is more often credited to Edward Banks of Deal in 1863.
1841 'Exoniensis' (*F. cordifolia* or *splendens* × 'Globosa'). A shrub with typical red and purple-blue fuchsia flowers. 'Exoniensis' now cultivated are usually 'Corallina'.
1842 'Corallina'. See p.58.
1852 (seedlings of 'Corallina'):
'Apollo': double; red and purple.
'Aspasia': trailing; single; red and purple.
'Princeps': crimson and purple.
1854 'Galanthiflora Plena' and
1855 'Florence Nightingale': William Storey claimed that these were stolen from him by a journeyman gardener and were identical with his 'Ranunculaeflora' and 'Mrs Storey' respectively.
1871 'Jeanie': semi-double; cerise and red.
1883 'Hallmark': single; white and red.

Bred by Stanborough Nursery, Elburton, Plymouth:
c.1980 'Birthday Girl'.

Bred by William H. Storey (or Story), White Hill, Newton Abbot (and his gardener Mr Brazier). Storey also bred Cape Heaths and Epacris:
1841 'Triumphans'.
'Formosa Elegans'.
1842 'Pulcherrima'.
1845 'Princess Victoria'.
1848 'Duplex': red and purple. The first double Fuchsia.
'Elegantissima': single; red and purple. Bred partly from *F. regia*.
'Mirabilis': single; red, and purple splashed red.
'Newtonensis'.
'Richard Mumford': semi-double; red and pink.
1850 'Ignaea': single; red and purple.
'Multiplex': double; red and purple-violet.
'South Devon': single; red and purple.
'Striata': single; red, and purple striped deep pink. The first striped Fuchsia.
1852 'Agnes': double; red and very dark purple.
'Aurora': single; elongated flower, red and deep purple.
'Fantome': double; short-tubed, red and violet-red.
'Peculiarity': double; red, and purple striped pink.
1853 'Prince Arthur'.
1854 'Lady of the Lake': red and pale pink.

The first red and white Fuchsias: all are single; crimson and white:
'Mrs Storey'.
'Queen Victoria'.
'Water Nymph'.

1855 'Dandy Dinmont': red and deep
violet.
'Empress Eugenie': red and white.
'Perugino': red, and purple striped
pink.
'Raffaelle': red, and chocolate
splashed pink. A strange colour,
otherwise unknown, if correctly
described.
'Ranunculaeflora': the first double
red and white fuchsia.
'Snowdrop': double; red and white.
1856 'Countess of Burlington': red and
white.
'Gem of Whitehill': red and deep
violet.
'Gloriosa Superba': red and deep
violet.
'Pilot': double; red and purple.
'Star': double; red and purple.
1859 'Governor General': red and purple.
1861 'Diamant': red and white.
'Esther Fearon': double; red and
pink.
1862 'James Shurvell': single; all red.

Bred by Robert Veitch & Son of Exeter:
'Pride of Orion'.
1852 'Dominyana' ('Dominiana') (*F.
macrostigma* × *denticulata*): bred by
Dominy. An autumn-flowering,
tender shrub with red flowers,
popular in Victorian winter gardens.
AM 1853.
1856 'Malakoff': double; crimson and
purple.
'Pendulina' (*F. simplicicaulis* ×
denticulata). Pendulous; red and pink
flowers, and 'ornamental foliage'.
1857 'Princess Royal': red and white.
1861 'Hugh Mollon': pink and purple.
1873 'Alexandrina': red and white.
1875 'Hugh Miller': single; pink and
purple.
1876 'Triumphant': pale red and deep
purple.
'Annie': single; pink and red. A.M.
1975.

1892 'Beauty of Exmouth': double; cerise
and white.
1894 'Ballet Girl': double; red and white.
AM 1894 and 1929.
1903 'Orpheus'.
'Sylvia': double; white and scarlet.

Gardenia (Rubiaceae). Evergreen shrubs and
trees. Funnel-shaped flowers, usually with a
superb fragrance. Warm greenhouse. The
following were sent to Lucombe, Pince & Co.
by Thomas Whitfield from Sierra Leone:
longistyla.
nitida. A bush 3 to 9 ft (1–3 m) high,
producing in early winter waxy pure white
flowers with a long slender tube and the
unusual number of seven narrow petal
segments "reflexed like birds in flight";
very fragrant and lasting only one day.
1844. Raised from seeds on a dried
specimen.

Gaultheria (Ericaceae)
nummularioides. 4–6 in. (10–15 cm) high,
spreading by underground shoots. Two
rows of small evergreen leaves. Small fat
flowers, white, pinkish or occasionally
brownish-red. Needs an acid soil and a
sheltered site. Introduced to Veitch from
the Khasia Hills of north India in 1850,
probably by Thomas Lobb.

Gazania (Compositae)
The 'Ebford Hybrids'. Some 60 cultivars
of the Treasure Flower were raised by
Gordon Ford at Ebford Nurseries,
Topsham between 1948 and 1965. They
were compact, floriferous and cushion-
forming, 6 to 12 in. (15–30 cm) high in
flower. Their colours included pink with
green centres; pink with black centres;
orange, white, red, yellow, and cream – all
with brown and emerald centres. Foliage
dark green, some cultivars dusted with
silver. Propagated by cuttings. Best on
sloping beds facing south as the flowers
only open in sunshine or very warm
conditions. Collections were supplied to

PLATE 130
Grevillea 'Semperflorens' at Bicton College, East Budleigh

Edinburgh, the Glasnevin Botanic Garden in Dublin, Calderstones Park in Liverpool, Glasgow, Hamburg, Pretoria and Johannesburg. They were planted round the Voortrekker Monument in South Africa in 1978, returned to their native land.

Gentiana (Gentianaceae)
asclepiadea 'Knightshayes'. This form of the Willow Gentian has deep blue trumpet flowers with conspicuous whitish throats, on more or less erect leafy stems to about 2½ ft (75 cm) tall in late summer. First recorded from Norman Hadden's garden at Porlock in Somerset, it is well-established at Knightshayes.
fascicularis (syn: *Crawfurdia fasciculata*). A climbing gentian from the Khasia Hills in north India. Funnel-shaped flowers to 1½ in. (4 cm) long, pale bluish-lilac, usually in September. To 8 ft (250 cm) or more. Sent by Thomas Lobb to Veitch, where it flowered in a glasshouse in 1855.

Geranium. See *Pelargonium*.

Gerbera (Compositae). Sir Michael Ansell, Pillhead Flower Farm, Northam, Bideford, raised 'Pillhead Inniskilling', 'Pillhead Sarah' and 'Pillhead Supreme' in the late 1940s.

Although blinded in the Second World War, he became Chairman of the Horse of the Year Show.

Gesneria (Gesneriaceae)
discolor. Introduced from Brazil in 1840 by William Lobb for Veitch.

'Exoniensis'. See *Smithiantha* 'Exoniensis'.

polyantha. Rich scarlet flowers, yellow inside, about 2 in. (5 cm) long, in drooping heads. Roots were sent from Brazil in 1840 by William Lobb to Veitch.

Gilia (Polemoniaceae). Five-petalled flowers, bell-shaped or flatter. Mostly herbaceous annuals to perennials. The following were introduced from California by William Lobb for Veitch:
californica. A low and spreading sub-shrub, the leaves with narrow fingers, and 1½ in. (4 cm) rosy-lilac flowers. Greenhouse.1854.
dianthoides. 2 to 5 in. (5–12cm) high with needle leaves. Flowers to 1½ in. (4 cm) long, with toothed or ragged edges, lilac or purplish, centre sometimes yellowish, July. Annual. 1855.
lutea. Leaves with narrow fingers; heads of yellow or orange flowers. Summer. Annual. To 1 ft (30 cm). 1852.

Gloxinia (Gesneriaceae). See *Sinningia*.

Gompholobium (Leguminosae). Evergreen shrubs with pea-flowers, needing perfect drainage and a cool greenhouse. Introduced from the Swan River area of S.W. Australia by Lucombe, Pince & Co.
latifolium (syn: *G. barbigerum*). The Broad Wedge-pea is native to sandy heaths. 3–4 ft (100–125 cm) high with large rich yellow flowers in June. 1824.
polymorphum 'Caulibus Purpureis'. Erect and twiggy, best when clipped, with purple stems and large rich deep red flowers. First flowered in UK in 1845.

Gomphrena (Amaranthaceae)
pulchella. An annual erect Globe
Amaranth with dense heads of small rose-
purple everlasting flowers. Introduced and
raised from seed imported from
Montevideo by Veitch, who first flowered
it in July 1844.

Grevillea (Proteaceae)
'Semperflorens'. To 6 ft (2 m) high in mild
gardens, with evergreen needle leaves and
clusters of spiky flowers that are orange-
yellow, touched with rose-pink and tipped
with green. It was raised by Miss F.E.
Briggs of Crown Hill, Plymouth, in 1926
by crossing *G. thelemanniana* and *G.
sulphurea*.

Griselinia (Cornaceae)
littoralis 'Luscombe's Gold'. The type is
an evergreen large shrub, or sometimes a
tree to 45ft (13.6 m), with wide glossy
leaves, not usually hardy outside mild
parts. 'Luscombe's Gold' has irregular
creamy-gold centres and bases to the
leaves, covering more than half their areas.
It is a sport of the more modestly marked
'Variegata' and arose at H.B. Luscombe's
wholesale nursery in 1970, then in
Torquay. It is slower growing than its
parent and should have green-leaved
shoots removed.

Habranthus pratensis (Amaryllidaceae).
See *Hippeastrum pratense*.

Hebe (Scrophulariaceae) Shrubby Veronica

'Carmine Princess'. A seedling of
'Midsummer Beauty', was raised by a
nurseryman at Sidford called Kitchener.

'Devonia' ('Devoniana'). Shining green
leaves and spikes of pinkish-purple flowers
summer and autumn. Raised by a gardener
calling himself 'Devonian' who sent a plant
to the editor of *Gardeners' Chronicle* in

1859. The original was then 4 × 22 ft
(125 × 700 cm). It was distributed as
Veronica decussata 'Devonia' (now *Hebe* ×
franciscana 'Devonia'), and is probably *H.
elliptica* × *speciosa*.

'Greenway Purple'. Large leaves and mid
bluish-purple flowers from late August.
2½ ft (75 cm). A chance seedling at
Greenway House, Galmpton.

'Miss E. Fittall'. 5–6 ft (1.75–2 m) high.
Light violet-blue flowers in dense narrow
spikes to 6 in. (15 cm) long from June to
November. Not very hardy. A parent of *H.*
'Midsummer Beauty' and the 'Wand'
hebes raised by Treseder of Truro. Raised
before 1960 by A. Andrews, VMH,
Superintendent of the Plymouth Parks,
and named after Eleanor, the daughter of
the Town Clerk.

'Primley Gem'. has spikes of violet-blue
flowers, ageing white, from July often until
November, and is fairly hardy. 'Margery
Fish' is a later name for the same plant; it
has also been called 'Primley Blue' and
'Morning Glory'. Raised at Herbert
Whitley's Primley Botanic Nursery in
Paignton, about the time of the Second
World War.

PLATE 131
Griselinia littoralis 'Luscombe's Gold' at Kiln House, Brixham

'Southcombe Pink'. About 4 ft (1.25 m) high; narrow leaves; late summer and autumn flowers, pink with white tubes, in 4 in. (10 cm) spikes. Hardier than most other pinks, and flourishing for 10 years at 900 ft (275 m) on Dartmoor, it nonetheless died there in early 1987 (though surviving in the lowlands). Chance seedling at Southcombe Gardens, Widecombe-in-the-Moor.

tetragona 'Southcombe Dwarf'. A bushy 6 in. (15 cm) high selection of a Whipcord Hebe which in the wild reaches 3 ft (1 m). Found at Southcombe Gardens, Widecombe-in-the-Moor.

'Veitchii'. A half-hardy bush with spikes of large violet flowers, raised by Veitch of Exeter a little before 1911. Most plants in cultivation are *H*. 'Alicia Amherst' (*H*. 'Royal Purple') which, although very similar, are probably not the same plant.

Hebecladus (Solanaceae)
biflorus (syn: *Atropa biflora*). Native of the Andes of Peru. Drooping tubular flowers, 1 in. (2.5 cm) long, purple with green segments. Greenhouse. Living specimens were sent by William Lobb to Exeter, where it flowered 1845.

PLATE 132
Helianthemum 'Georgeham' at Little Southey, Northcott

Helianthemum (Cistaceae)
'Georgeham'. Cerise-red flowers with yellow centres, May onwards. Vigorous. Raised at the now defunct Four Winds Nursery, Georgeham.

Helleborus (Ranunculaceae) Lenten Rose T.H. Archer Hind of Coombe Fishacre near Ipplepen had an extensive collection in the 1880s and by crossing at least *orientalis*, *abchasicus* and *guttatus* raised, among others:

'Coombe Fishacre Purple', with deep plum-coloured flowers, was still in cultivation in 1958 according to Margery Fish.

'Coombe Fishacre Yellow'. Greenish-yellow flowers.

'Primrose Dame'. As above.

Heterotrichum (Melastomataceae)
macrodon. Hot-house shrub attaining 8 ft (250 cm), but producing even when quite young its showy autumn flowers, pure white with red bases. The twigs and big leaves are covered with reddish hairs. Introduced from Colombia by William Lobb for Veitch.

Hindsia (Rubiaceae). Small evergreen hot-house shrubs, the tops of the twigs bearing bunches of long tubular flowers opening star-like at the mouths. Introduced by William Lobb for Veitch:
longiflora. Bright blue (occasionally white) flowers. To 2 ft (60 cm). Brazil. 1842.
violacea. Deep porcelain-violet flowers. 3 ft (1 m) high. South Brazil. 1843.

Hippeastrum (Amaryllidaceae)
pratense (syn: *Habranthus pratensis*) Large scarlet flowers, usually veined yellow at the base, on stems to 1 ft (30 cm) or so, in May. Hardy in mildest places. Sent to Veitch from Valdivia in Chile; they first flowered it in 1842.

Hosta (Liliaceae)
sieboldiana 'Golden'. Large, rather heart-shaped leaves of deep yellow with strong ribs. A sport of 'Frances Williams' at The Garden House, Buckland Monachorum.

PLATE 133
Hoya bella

Hoya (Asclepiadaceae). Evergreen shrubs, mostly climbers, found from India to China and Australia. Waxy flowers in heads. Greenhouse. Introduced to Veitch by Thomas Lobb:

bella. See p.59.
cinnamomifolia. See p.59.
coriacea. Leathery leaves. Large heads of brownish-yellow flowers. Java. 1838.
coronaria. Flowers about 1½ in. (3.5 cm) across, yellowish, speckled purple, the central petals ivory white. Hairy leaves. Java. 1856.
cumingiana. An evergreen climber. Flower greenish-yellow or white with a rich purplish-brown ring around the centre. Introduced from Malaya to Veitch, who first flowered it in about 1849.
fraterna. Leaves to 1 ft (30 cm) or more long. Pale buff flowers, stained red centrally. Java. 1851.
purpureo-fusca. Silver-Pink Vine. White-haired rusty-red flowers with purple central petals; in large dense heads in September. Leaves with raised pinkish-silver blotches. Java. 1849.

Hulthemia and × **Hulthemosa** (Rosaceae)
See *Rosa* 'Edward Hyams'.

Humata (Polypodiaceae). See *Davallia*.

Hyacinthoides hispanicus 'Chevithorne' (Liliaceae). See p.59.

Hydrangea (Hydrangeaceae)

paniculata 'Kalmthout'. A vigorous, branching, hardy shrub to 5 ft (1.5 m) with large creamy-white flowers in summer. A seedling selected by Mr & Mrs Robert de Belder at the Kalmthout Arboretum in Belgium, introduced and named by the Lady Anne Palmer at Rosemoor.

'Veitchii' has lace-cap flower heads with large white outer and small blue inner flowers. First exhibited by Veitch of Exeter at the Temple Show in 1903, it had been imported from Japan. AM 1974.

Hypericum (Hypericaceae)
lobbii. Sometimes identified as *H. oblongifolium* or *H. hookerianum*, it was introduced from Assam by, and in 1970 finally named after, Thomas Lobb, collecting for Veitch of Exeter. A shrub with bright yellow flowers from August to October, needing shelter.

Hypocalymma (Myrtaceae)
robustum. The Peach Myrtle is a small Australian bush with narrow evergreen leaves in pairs, and ½ in. (1.2 cm) flowers of rich pink with many stamens, in leafy spikes up to 10 in. (4 cm) long. Hardy in the Isles of Scilly, but elsewhere needs a cool greenhouse and a sandy soil. Introduced by Lucombe, Pince & Co. in 1843.

Hypocyrta (Gesneriaceae)
strigillosa. A hairy, erect 2 ft (60 cm) high shrub with scarlet and yellow swollen-tubed flowers, found on anthills and decaying tree-trunks in the Organ Mountains of Brazil. Greenhouse. Introduced in 1843 by William Lobb for Veitch.

Ilex (Aquifoliaceae) Holly

aquifolium 'Fred Harris'. A reversed sport on *I.a.* 'Argentea-marginata' was found at the now closed W.H. Harris Ltd's Westacott Nursery near Barnstaple in 1973 and named after the owner. The leaves have white centres.

'Woodside'. A sport on *I.a.* 'Ferox Argentea', the variegated hedgehog holly, with white leaf centres, found in Dorset and propagated by Mervyn Feesey of Barnstaple.

Impatiens (Balsaminaceae)

platypetala. An annual Balsam with large rose-coloured flowers, each with a very slender, sickle-shaped spur; on 1½ ft+ (18 cm) stems that are usually reddish-purple. Summer. Sent to Veitch from Java, probably by Thomas Lobb, in 1844.

Iris (Iridaceae)

'Bourne Elegant'. Lavender flowers, the lower petals with mauve markings and spots around an orange-yellow crest, on about 20 in. (50 cm) stems. Semi-shade, a fertile slightly acid soil and a mild climate. *I. japonica* was crossed with *I. confusa* by Dr Ellis at University of London. A.J.R. Bailey of Paignton grew on some of the seedlings and for one, 'Bourne Elegant' obtained an AM in 1985.

'Dominion' was raised in Devon by the amateur A.J. Bliss in 1917. It was the first tall bearded Iris with a velvet texture to the flowers. From seed of 'Dominion' he raised, among others:

'Majestic'. Large flowers on 32 in. (80 cm) stems; lavender-violet standards, rich velvety purplish-violet falls. Before 1923. AM 1930.

'Pendragon'. Flowers on 30 in. (75 cm) stems; smoky reddish-violet standards with yellowish base; rich plum-purple falls. Before 1924. AM 1930.

'Swazi'. 3 ft (90 cm). Bright violet standards, falls deep rich velvety violet. Before 1922. AM 1930.

'Zulu'. 3 ft (90 cm). Lavender violet standards, deep rich violet-blue falls. Before 1925. AM 1930.

Bliss also raised:

'Blue Lagoon' with lavender standards, violet blue falls with blue-veined white bases, central beard white tipped with yellow; 30 in. (75 cm) stems. Before 1919.

ensata (syn: *I. kaempferi*) 'Rowden'. White flowers with blue and violet standard petals in June or July. Raised by John Carter at Rowden Gardens, Brentor.

laevigata 'Violet Garth'. This sport occured recently in seedlings at Mr & Mrs John Carter's Rowden Gardens, Brentor. It needs a wet soil or shallow water, has pale pinkish-violet flowers in June or July.

sibirica 'Southcombe White'. White flowers, the falls slightly mauve-violet, their bases brown-yellow netted darker; about 3 ft (1 m) high. May to June. Raised at Southcombe Gardens, Widecombe-in-the-Moor, in the late 1970s.

unguicularis 'Mary Barnard'. See p.62.

A. Boker

PLATE 134
Iris sibirica 'Southcombe White' at Southcombe Gardens, Widecombe

Ixora (Rubiaceae). Handsome evergreen hot-house shrubs with tight heads of long slender-tubed flowers, with 4 spreading petals at their mouths.

acuminata. 3–6 ft (1–2 m) tall. Fragrant white flowers with 1½ in. (4 cm) long tubes. Introduced by Thomas Lobb for Veitch from North India.

floribunda. Bright reddish-scarlet flowers in large trusses. Introduced by Thomas Lobb for Veitch from Java.

fulgens. See *I. salicifolia.*

javanica. Jungle Geranium. To 4 ft (120 cm); coral-red branches; orange-red (occasionally pink or yellow) waxy flowers, scentless as they are pollinated by birds. Introduced in 1846 from Java by Thomas Lobb for Veitch.

laxiflora. 3–4 ft (100–125 cm) high with very fragrant flowers with a 1½ in. (4 cm) long tube arising from the deep red calyx and ending in white petals that are fringed with pink; in large clusters. Summer. Sent from Sierra Leone to Lucombe, Pince & Co. in about 1850.

lobbii. Bright orange-scarlet flowers. Introduced by Thomas Lobb to Veitch, from the mountains of Java.

odorata. Broad leaves to 9 in. (22 cm) long, similar in texture to those of the Rubber Plant (*Ficus elastica*). Deliciously fragrant flowers to 5 in. (12.5 cm) long, the tube red at its base, white above, the petal lobes white, soon ageing buff and twisted; July–August. Introduced from Madagascar, via the Continent, by Lucombe, Pince & Co. in 1843 or slightly before.

salicifolia. Often misidentified as *I. fulgens.* Long narrow leaves. Orange-scarlet flowers. Introduced from Java in 1850 by Thomas Lobb for Veitch.

Juniperus (Cupressaceae) Juniper

californica. The Californian Juniper is a small tree with spreading branches and scale-like yellowish-green leaves. It is tender, at least when young, and is adapted to arid land. Introduced in 1853 by William Lobb collecting for Veitch of Exeter.

communis 'Zeal'. A form of the Common Juniper reaching about 20 in. (50 cm) high and more than twice as wide, with upright growths. Raised at Knightshayes from a seedling given by E.B. Anderson from his garden in West Somerset. Zeal is the former name of the land on which Knightshayes stands.

Kniphofia (Liliaceae) Red-Hot Poker

'Mermaiden'. See p.63.

'Zeal Primrose'. Widely spaced creamy primrose flowers on 30 in. (75 cm) stems in June and July. A seedling of *K.* 'Limelight' with some *K. snowdenii* blood, raised by Terry Jones of Zeal Monachorum near Crediton, recently, and given to Jane Taylor who named it while head gardener at Coleton Fishacre, Kingswear.

× **Laeliocattleya** 'Exoniensis'. Included in *Cattleya.*

Lapageria rosea (Philesiaceae). See p.64.
rosea albiflora. See p.64.

Lardizabala (Lardizabalaceae)
biternata. A twining climber to 12 ft (4 m); evergreen leaves with leaflets in threes. The flowers have large chocolate-purple fleshy sepals and small white petals. On male plants they are ¾ in. (2 cm) across and in drooping clusters. Female flowers are solitary and a little larger; if a male plant is near, 2–3 in. (5–7.5 cm) long edible fleshy purple fruits may be produced. Greenhouse, or sheltered wall in mildest climate. William Lobb obtained a plant from Thomas Davey in Chile and sent it to Veitch in 1844.

Larix (Pinaceae)
kaempferi 'Cruwys Morchard'. Found and

propagated from a Witch's Broom on a
Japanese Larch tree at Cruwys Morchard,
near Tiverton, by Gordon Haddow of
Kenwith Castle Nurseries, Bideford. It has
grown about 2½ ft (75 cm) high and 1½ ft
(45 cm) wide in 10 years.

Leschenaultia (Goodeniaceae). Heath-like
plants from Australia with showy flowers
looking like tubes split down 5 ways and
opened flat, needing a sandy compost and a
greenhouse.
  biloba. A 2–3 ft (60–90 cm) high evergreen
  bush with brilliant blue flowers, 1 in.
  (2.5 cm) + across, from June to August.
  Raised by Veitch from seed sent by James
  Drummond from West Australia in 1840.
  laricina (syn: *L. splendens*). 1–2 ft (30–
  60 cm) high, with greyish-green needle
  leaves and 1¼ in. (3 cm) flowers that vary
  from white or lilac to rich red with yellow
  bases. Introduced by Lucombe, Pince &
  Co. in 1844.
  linarioides (syn: *L. arcuata*). To 2 ft
  (60 cm) high or less; the upper lip of the
  flower is sulphur-yellow, the smaller lower
  lip red-purple. Introduced by Lucombe,
  Pince & Co. in 1844.

Leucostegia (Polypodiaceae). See *Davallia*.

Leucothoe (Ericaceae)
  davisiae. An evergreen shrub, 3 ft (1 m) or
  less high, with spikes of small white bell-
  flowers in June, needing a lime-free soil
  and preferring part shade. Discovered and
  collected in California by William Lobb
  for Veitch of Exeter in 1853. FCC 1883.

Libocedrus (Cupressaceae)
  uvifera (syn: *Libocedrus tetragona* and
  Pilgerodendron uviferum). A tree,
  reminiscent of *Chamaecyparis lawsoniana*
  'Wisselii' with its twisted spires of foliage.
  It has reached 28 ft (8.5 m) in Ireland.
  Introduced from Chile in 1849 by William
  Lobb for Veitch of Exeter.

Lilium (Liliaceae) Lily
  Raised by Mr & Mrs R.J. Holmes of
  Sidbury. Gerald Derby gave them seed of
  L. Shakespeare strain. Among the
  seedlings raised was a cream flowered
  plant which they crossed with the Yellow
  Tiger Lily (L. 'Flaviflorum'). Among the
  progeny they selected, in about 1970:
    'Brampford Rose' with old-rose-pink
    turks-cap flowers on stems to 3 ft (1 m),

    'Devonshire Cream' with pale cream
    flowers spotted purple.

  neilgherrense. The narrow funnel-flowers
  are fragrant, up to 10 in.
  (25 cm) long, white with some yellow
  inside, 2 or 3 on each 2 to 4 ft (60–
  120 cm) rooting stem. Underground
  runners. The southernmost lily.
  Greenhouse. Collected by Thomas Lobb
  in the Nilghiri Hills in southern India in
  the 1860s, it failed to become established
  in the U.K.
  × *testaceum* Mary Lees strain. See p.65.

  Raised by Derek Gardham, Blackdown
  Lilies, Newton Poppleford. See also p.65.

    'Blackdown Gold'. Golden trumpet
    lily.

    'Blackdown Late Gold'. Dark yellow
    trumpet lily.

    'Devon Butter.' A dwarf yellow lily
    about 1 ft (30 cm) tall.

    'Devon Dawn Hybrids'. See p.65.

    'Honeysuckle Rose'. Pink trumpet lily.

  longiflorum 'Coral Reef Strain'. See
  p.65.

    'Silver Swan'.

Linum (Linaceae)
  chamissonis. An orange-flowered flax,
  woody at the base, not hardy. Introduced
  from Chile by Pearce from his 1859–62
  collecting for Veitch of Exeter.

Loasa (Loasaceae)

picta. An annual about 1 ft (30 cm) high, with even the flowers covered with stinging hairs, contact with which for most people is a temporary irritant, for a few a durable rash. Yellow and white flowers with hood-like petals, in leafy heads. Sent from the Peruvian Andes by William Lobb to Veitch in 1848.

Lobbia dependens (Aristolochiaceae). See *Thottea dependens.*

Lomatia ferruginea (Proteaceae). See p.68.

Luculia (Rubiaceae)

pinceana. A shrub to 6 ft (2 m) tall with very fragrant flowers, white, ageing creamy-blush inside, deep pink outside, to 2 in. (5 cm) across, on a slender tube to 2 in. (5 cm) long, in clusters. May to September. Greenhouse. Raised in 1841 by Robert Pince of Lucombe, Pince & Co., from seed from the Khasia Hills in north India.

Lygodium (Schizaeaceae)

polystachyum. A greenhouse climbing fern with large interlacing fronds. Introduced from Burma by Thomas Lobb for Veitch of Exeter.

Macleania (Ericaceae)

punctata. A low shrub from the Andes of Ecuador. Neat evergreen leaves with translucent dots. Bright scarlet tubular flowers 1¼ in. (3 cm) long, tipped yellow in bud and white when open. Grey berries, flushed pink. Warm greenhouse and a non-limy peaty soil. Sent by William Lobb to Veitch, who first flowered it in 1848.

Magnolia (Magnoliaceae)

campbellii 'Sidbury'. See p.68.
grandiflora 'Exmouth'. See p.69.
× *soulangeana* 'Coimbra'. See p.69.
× *veitchii* 'Isca' & 'Peter Veitch'. See p.69.

PLATE 135
Leschenaultia biloba

G. Beckett

Mahonia (Berberidaceae)
'Buckland'. See p.70.
'Lionel Fortescue'. See p.70.

Malus domestica (Rosaceae) Apple (Quotations marked H.V.T. are from H.V. Taylor's *The Apples of England* published by Crosby, Lockwood in 1948.)

'Allspice' "a dessert apple grown in Devonshire. Similar in size and shape to 'Duke of Devonshire'." H.V.T.

'Barum Beauty'. A seedling raised by W.G. Davies of Landkey before 1979.

'Bowden's Seedling'. See p.72.

'Cerit'. "A Devonshire apple of medium culinary size; round, somewhat conical and angular; skin clear yellow-green, with russet markings on the base and in the stem cavity." H.V.T.

'Crimson Costard'. "Grown at Paignton, Devon. A medium-size apple, very tall and somewhat like 'Mother'. Differs in that the eye is usually large and open. A second-rate dessert apple." H.V.T.

'Devon Crimson Queen'. Origin unknown, before 1953. Yellow apples much flushed bright red.

'Devonshire Buckland'. First recorded in 1831 from Devon. Pale yellow apples with orange brown to pink flush.

'Devonshire Court Pendu'. Origin unknown, before 1883.

'Devonshire Golden Ball'. Origin unknown, before 1831. Large late apples with light yellow skins, flushed and striped crimson.

'Devonshire Quarrendon'. See p.70.
'Devonshire Queen'. Origin unknown, before 1820. Bright yellow apples, flushed and striped crimson.

'Devonshire Red Streak'. A Devon apple first described in 1831. Pale yellow fruit, striped scarlet. Late flowering.

'Devonshire Striped'. Unknown origin, before 1883. Russet coloured apples, streaked red.

'Devonshire White Sour'. Unknown origin, before 1831. Small greenish-yellow apples.

'Docker's Devonshire'. Origin before 1820. Red-striped apples.

'Lucombe's Pine'. Produced by William Lucombe's nursery in the early nineteenth century. Pale yellow, tinged orange with russet dots, having a rich aromatic pineapple flavour.

'Lucombe's Seedling'. From Lucombe's nursery before 1831. Pale greenish-yellow, flushed and streaked bright red, with a spicy, rather acid flavour.

'Michaelmas Stubbard'. "A Devonshire apple. Oblong, tall and flattened at both ends. Colour yellow-green, with a brownish-red flush. Eye large, closed in a very ribbed basin. Long stem. An early and popular dessert apple for August. Distinctive flavour." H.V.T.

'Paignton Marigold'. "Similar to 'Beauty of Bath' in shape, but the colour is deeper and more intense, and it is probably a later keeping apple." H.V.T.

'Peter Lock'. See p.70.

'Plympton King'. "Much grown in Cornwall. A pea-green apple, in shape similar to a 'Bramley Seedling'. A few red streaks. The eye is in a wrinkled basin of deeper green. Stem very stout in a very wide cavity. Russet markings in the stem cavity and on base of fruit. Season: a good late cooker – till March & April." H.V.T.

'Ponsford'. "A Devonshire cider apple often used for cooking. Somewhat like a small green 'Bramley Seedling'." H.V.T.

'Pyne's Pearmaine'. Raised by George Pyne, Denver Nurseries, Topsham, before 1948.

'Quench' ('Quince'). "A tall, conical apple of large dessert size, grown in Devon. Skin green, with occasional orange-red flush and scarlet streaks on the base. Eye closed in a deep puckered basin. Stem short, embedded in a russet cavity." H.V.T.

'Red Ribbed Greening'. "Grown in Devon and often wrongly named 'Cornish Gilliflower'. It is more irregular and like 'Costard'. Season: ripe December." H.V.T.

'Star of Devon'. See p.70.

'Tom Potter'. A Devon apple from before 1831. Yellow fruit, striped and blotched bright red.

'Upton Pyne'. Raised, and introduced in 1910, by George Pyne. "Of very distinct flavour and likely to become popular." (E.A. Bunyard).

'Woolbrook Pippin'. See p.72.

'Woolbrook Russet'. See p.72.

Malva sylvestris 'Primley Blue' (Malvaceae)
See p.72.

Mandevilla hispida (Apocynaceae). See
Dipladenia hirsuta.

Manettia (Rubiaceae)
 bicolor. Firecracker Plant. A trailing or
 climbing evergreen with thread-like stems,
 from the Organ Mountains of Brazil.
 Flask-like flowers a waxy vivid yellow,
 mostly densely covered with bright scarlet
 bristles, so as to appear red tipped with
 yellow; ¾ in. (2 cm) long, in March.
 Warm greenhouse. Introduced in 1843 by
 William Lobb for Veitch.

Matthewsii glauca (Ericaceae)
 See *Befaria glauca tomentella.*

Medinilla (Melastomataceae). The following
are evergreen hot-house shrubs, with
drooping sprays of flowers, needing a light
organic soil, moisture and heat; collected by
Thomas Lobb for Veitch.
 magnifica. Rose Grape. To 6 ft (2 m).
 Polished leaves to 12 x 8 in. (30 x 20 cm).
 Purple anthers on yellow filaments in the
 centres of rosy-pink flowers, long-lasting
 and beautiful, whose clusters hang on a
 pinkish stalk from large pinkish leaf-like
 bracts. Philippines 1849.
 speciosa. About 3 ft (1 m). Pale red flowers
 with deeper coloured edges. Java 1845.

PLATE 136
Medinilla magnifica

PLATE 137
Mitraria coccinea at Bicton College, East Budleigh

Mimulus (Scrophulariaceae)
 cupreus. Tufted habit; flowers at first
 yellow, becoming copper-coloured; throat
 yellow, spotted brown. 8–12 in. (20–30
 cm) high. The parent of many hybrids.
 Sent from the Chilean Andes in 1861 by
 Richard Pearce for Veitch of Exeter.

Mitraria (Gesneriaceae)
 coccinea. Evergreen shrub, spreading, or
 climbing by ivy-like aerial roots to 20 ft (6
 m) or so. Small polished leaves. Scarlet
 tubular flowers to 1¼ in. (3 cm) long, from
 May sporadically until autumn. Cool moist
 spot in an equable climate. Introduced by
 William Lobb for Veitch from the rain
 forests of Chile in 1846. A recent
 introduction produces more flowers and is
 probably hardier.

Mutisia decurrens (Compositae). See p.72.

Myrtus (Myrtaceae). Myrtle. Evergreen woody plants; white flowers (occasionally pinkish) with many central stamens. The following were introduced from Chile by William Lobb to Veitch:

chequen. See p.74.
luma (syn: *apiculata)*. See p.73.
ugni. See p.73.

Naegelia 'Exoniensis' (Gesneriaceae). See *Smithiantha.*

Narcissus (Amaryllidaceae) Daffodil
Raised by Thomas Batson, Beaworthy near Okehampton, between 1896–1918:
'Actis'.
'Argos'.
'Beaworthy'.
'Chlora'.
'Chryseis'.
'Clottro'.
'Clyto'.
'Cymry'.
'Demeter'.

Raised by Arthur Bliss of Morwellham, between 1923–30:
'Amoy'.
'Benbow'.
'Bertrand'.
'Caradon'.
'Ingot'.
'Iona'.

Raised by the Rev. Thomas Buncombe, Black Torrington, between 1906–41:
'Chepstow'.
'Coham'.
'Corporal'.

Raised by Sir Charles Cave, Bart., Sidbury Manor, between 1897–1932:
'Agamemnon'.

'Ambition'.
'Ambush'.
'Anne Boleyn'.
'Beethoven'.
'Bloodhound'.
'Bloodstone'.
'Brilliant'.
'Capacity'.
'Chamois'.
'Climax'.
'Competition'.
'Conference'.
'Count Palatine'.
'Credit'.
'Cynthia'.
'Dab-chick'.
'Daphne'.
'Falcon'.
'Flora'.
'Grenadier'.
'Indus' AM 1932.
'Memory'.
'Music'.
'Queen of Dawn' AM 1917.
"Red Riding Hood".
'Ruby' 1907.
'Wildfire'.

Raised at E.B. Champernowne, Green Lane Gardens, Buckland Monachorum:
'Burrator'.
'Queensland'. See p.74.
'Red Devon'. See p.74.
'Red Lake'. See p.74.
'Reed Warbler' 1948.
'Sarah'.

Raised by Mr and Mrs Roger Cobley, Chircombe, Bideford, and sometime after 1938 at Seymour-Cobley Ltd, Braunton:
'Anak' 1932.
'Beltone' before 1938.
'Bikkur' 1932.
'Cinnamon' 1932.
'Circa' 1937
'Comrie' 1968.
'Constance Morel' 1937.
'Cullen' 1968.

'Dandelion' 1938.
'Dayspring' 1937.
'Denia' 1937.
'Devon' 1937.
'Dunvegan'.
'Earlish' 1968
'Eden' 1968.
'Epigram' 1938.
'Fire Opal' 1937.
'Greensleeves' 1932.
'Huguenot' 1932.
'Huntercombe' AM 1938.
'Inverurie' 1954.
'Jimmy Taylor' 1968.
'John Henry Taylor' 1943.
'Lilibet' 1937.
'Malory' 1937.
'Nenone' 1954.
'Peorocita' 1937.
'Pendragon' 1932.
'Poise' before 1938.
'Popinjay' 1937.
'Portjoy' before 1967.
'Ruanda' 1937.
'Sandra' before 1954.
'Seymour Cobley' 1968
'Silence' 1932.
'Silver Ghost' 1937.
'Silver Tips' before 1954.
'Six of Spades' 1944.
'Winter Glow' 1932.
'Yellow Carpet' before 1954.
'Yorkist' 1932.

Raised by Miss Kathy Hinchcliff (1861–1948), Worlington House, Instow. She was a friend of the Cobleys. Her collection of butterflies and moths is in the Exeter Museum and many of her photographs of Devon churches have been used in Diocesan records. She exhibited at RHS Daffodil Shows and before the Second World War ran the Instow Flower Show, without prizes, judges, entrance fees, rigid classifications or committee:
'Colmartin' 1937.
'Day a Peep' 1939.
'Dead White' 1943.

'Dinofor' 1935.
'Donald Richardson' 1941.
'Forelli' 1937.
'Frothy Ale' 1935.
'Grace Cobley' 1937.
'Instow' 1935.
'King Peter' 1941.
'Kitty Crowley' 1941.
'Mary Cobley' 1941.
'Red Pedestal' 1940.
'Spun Gold' 1932.
'Surf' 1932.
'Tudor Rose' 1937.
'Worlington' 1930. AM 1939.

Raised by John Kendall, Newton Poppleford:
'King Alfred' See p. 74.

Raised by Dr Norman Lock, Exeter (later Budleigh Salterton):
'Erda' 1944.
'Fafnir' 1944.
'Flosshilde' 1944.
'Freia' 1944. AM 1948
'Fricka' 1944.
'Jennifer Susan' 1942.
'Nedda' 1944.
'Pamina' 1944.
'Petronella' 1944.
'Senta' 1944.
'Sieglinde' 1944.
'Walraute' 1944.

Raised by Peter Lower, Teignmouth:
'Askival'. See p.75.

Narcissus pseudo-narcissus
(Amaryllidaceae) See p.74.

Nepenthes (Nepenthaceae) Pitcher Plant Greenhouse. The species below were introduced to Veitch by Thomas Lobb. (See also p.75.)

albo-marginata. A dwarf plant with leaves to 1 ft (30 cm) long, the pitchers with pale green bases, reddish tops and a white ring near the mouth. Singapore 1848.

'Dominii' ('Dominiana'). The first hybrid Pitcher plant, raised at the Exeter Veitch nursery by John Dominy in 1862. It has broad dark green leaves and spotted deep green pitchers to 6 in. (15 cm) long. A *Nepenthes rafflesiana* hybrid.

sanguinea. Thick stalkless leaves. Deep blood-red (occasionally reddish-green) pitchers to 10 in. (25 cm) long and 3 in. (7.5 cm) across. Malaya 1849.

veitchii. Yellow-green pitchers to 8 in. (20 cm) long, the rim of the mouth with scarlet ribs. Borneo 1847.

Nerine (Amaryllidaceae)
bowdenii. See p.76
'Exonia'. See p.77
'Marney Rogerson'. See p.77.
'Zeal Damson', 'Zeal Giant' and 'Zeal Plush'. See p.77.

Nothofagus (Fagaceae)
obliqua. Southern Beech, Roblé. Although its introduction is usually credited to William Lobb, it is not now clear what plant he sent to Veitch as *Fagus obliqua*. The most likely candidate is *N. betuloides*, which would have been a reintroduction.

Nymphaea (Nymphaeaceae)
lotus dentata (syn: *N. dentata*). A variety of the Sacred Lotus, a water-lily, with leaves often 2 ft (60 cm) across and pure white flowers to 14 in. (35 cm) across in autumn. Greenhouse. Introduced from Sierra Leone in 1845 by Lucombe, Pince & Co.

× **Odontioda** 'Honiton Lace' (Orchidaceae). See p.82.

Odontoglossum bictoniense (Orchidaceae). See p.81.

Oenothera (Onagraceae)
bistorta veitchiana. Southern Sun Cups. An annual to 2 ft (60 cm) tall with daytime evening-primrose flowers, lemon-yellow from red buds. Contorted seed pods to 1½ in. (3.5 cm) long. Coasts of south California. Introduced by William Lobb for Veitch in 1858.

Olearia (Compositae)
× *haastii.* A natural hybrid of *O. avicenniaefolia* and *O. moschata* from New Zealand. An evergreen bush with fragrant white daisy flowers in July and August; one of the hardier olearias, though unreliable in some areas. FCC 1873, AGM 1928. Introduced by Veitch of Exeter in 1858.

Oncidium (Orchidaceae)
curtum. Yellow flowers much marked cinnamon-brown, in spikes to 3½ ft (110 cm), spring. Greenhouse. Introduced from Brazil in 1841–2 by William Lobb for Veitch.

Origanum 'Buckland' (Labiatae). See p.83.

Osmanthus (Oleaceae)
heterophyllus. A holly-like slowly growing large shrub with small white autumnal flowers that are sweetly scented. Native to Japan and Taiwan, introduced for Veitch of Exeter by Thomas Lobb in 1856. FCC 1859.

Osteospermum (syn: *Dimorphotheca*) (Compositae) Veld Daisy
'Langtrees'. A surprisingly hardy plant, low growing, with bright purple-pink flowers all summer. From Dr Rogerson's garden, Langtrees.
'Weetwood'. Prostrate and hardier than most, with large white flowers with green backs. Suitable for ground cover in a sunny well-drained spot. Harold Bawden named 'Weetwood' after his garden at Offwell near Honiton where this chance cross of *O. ecklonis* and *O. jucunda* occurred.

Ourisia (Scrophulariaceae). Slowly creeping with low leaves and heads of tubular flowers; needing a moist well-drained soil, dryish in the winter, a cool spot and a moderate climate:

coccinea. Bright scarlet flowers, nodding, 1½ in. (3.5 cm) long, on stems to 1 ft+ (30 cm). Introduced from the Chilean Andes by William Lobb for Veitch of Exeter in 1849.

pearcei. Crimson flowers, streaked blood-red, larger than *O. coccinea.* Leaves with purplish undersides. Introduced from the Chilean Andes by Richard Pearce for Veitch of Exeter. FCC 1863.

Oxalis (Oxalidaceae)

elegans. Small clover leaves with purplish undersides. Purple flowers with a deeper coloured ring in the throat, funnel-shaped, nearly 1 in. (2.5 cm) long, on stems to 1 ft (30 cm), July. Introduced by William Lobb from Peru in 1848 for Veitch.

Paphiopedilum (syn: *Cypripedium*) (Orchidaceae). Slipper Orchid, so called for the fancied resemblance of the prominent pouch-like lip of the flower to that footwear. Warm greenhouse. Introduced by Thomas Lobb for Veitch.

barbatum has whitish flowers, striped and stained purple with black hairs, shining black lumps on the top edge of the petals, and a large pouched black-purple lip. Light green leaves with random scatterings of very dark green. About 1 ft (30 cm) high. Malaya 1843.

javanicum. Flowers 3 in. (7.5 cm) high, pale green; petals marked matt purple and dotted blackish; brownish-green pouch, spotted purple on the sides. Chequered leaves. Java 1840.

villosum. Flowers to 5 in. (12 cm) or more across, polished; the green backs are bordered with white and lined with purplish-brown; the yellowish-brown fronts have a purple mid-line and a

brownish-yellow stuck-out lip; October to March; on 6–12 in. (15–30 cm) hairy stems. Introduced from Moulmein.

Parahebe (Scrophulariaceae)

'Mervyn'. A few inches high with pale blue flowers veined reddish. Grown from seed by Mervyn Feesey of Barnstaple in 1963 and named by Graham Hutchins of County Park Nurseries, Hornchurch, Essex.

Passiflora (Passifloraceae). Passion Flower, named, not as an aphrodisiac, but because parts of the plant reminded Spanish priests in South America of accessories of the Crucifixion. Climbing by twining tendrils.

actinia. Named for its resemblance to a sea-anemone. 3 in. (7.5 cm) fragrant white flowers full of 1½ in. (3.5 cm) long, incurved and twisted filaments banded white, red and blue; spring and summer. Collected in Brazil by William Lobb for Veitch in 1841.

antioquiensis (syn: *Tacsonia van volxemii*). See p.83.

× *'Exoniensis'.* See p.83.

mollissima. See p.83.

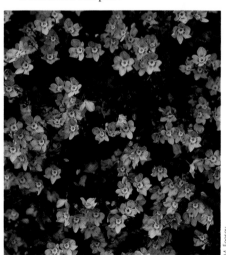

M. Feesey

PLATE 138
Parahebe 'Mervyn' at Woodside, near Barnstaple

Pelargonium (Geraniaceae)
'Formosa'. Rose-pink flowers with a large velvet clouded spot edged crimson on the upper part. Raised by Veitch before 1843.

'Gem of the West'. Dark red upper petals, with paler edges; pale pink lower petals, with dark veins and a white centre. This was raised in 1840 by Mr Nairn of Stoke, now in Plymouth. He also raised 'Arabella', 'Cressida', 'Mabel' and 'Nairn's Success'.

'Thurtell's Pluto'. Raised by Capt C. Thurtell RN of Somerset Place, Stoke, Plymouth, before 1843. Most likely the parent of all the subsequently raised plants that have dark flowers with velvety blotches. He also raised 'Thurtell's Defiance', 'Thurtell's Horatio Nelson' and 'Thurtell's Queen', all with white or pale pink flowers, that have a crimson-edged dark blotch, and all shown by Lucombe, Pince & Co. in 1843.

Lucombe, Pince & Co. introduced 'Black Prince', 'British Queen', 'Cleopatra', 'Evening Star', 'Leonora', 'Meteor', 'Susanna', mostly with dark flowers, in 1844.

'Torbay Delight'. A useful and most attractive early flowering mixture in various shades of red, salmon and pink, red and white, and white, for beds, borders and containers. Compact and uniform, about 1 ft (30 cm) high, the plants flower steadily from July until late autumn. Raised by Suttons Seeds Ltd of Torquay in the 1980s.

Pennisetum alopecuroides 'Woodside' (Gramineae). See p.86.

Penstemon (Scrophulariaceae) Beard Tongue
cyananthus. Conical heads of bright blue flowers in August; to 3 ft (1 m) high. Introduced from the Rocky Mountains by Lucombe, Pince & Co. in about 1849.

jaffrayanus. Large rich blue flowers, reddish at their bases and in their throats, August. 1 ft (30 cm) high. First found by Mr Jaffray in north California in 1853. Introduced by William Lobb to Veitch, where it first flowered in 1857.

'Torbay Gem'. Glowing postbox-red narrow flowers about 1½ in. (3.5 cm) long. One of the hardiest. Given to Coleton Fishacre about 1950 by George Cousin VMH, Superintendent of Torquay Parks, and probably raised by him.

Pentapterygium rugosum (Ericaceae) See *Agapetes incurvata.*

Perezia (Compositae)
viscosa. An annual with leaves mostly low down. Purple daisies atop 1½ft (45 cm) stems in June. Seeds with reddish hairs. Introduced by Pearce from Chile in 1862 for Veitch.

Phacelia (Hydrophyllaceae)
minor (syn: *P. whitlavia*). California Bells. An annual, 6–24 in. (15–60 cm) high, with bright blue bell-flowers in clusters, preferring a sunny spot and a dryish soil. Avoid spring frosts. Discovered by Douglas, and introduced to Veitch by William Lobb in 1854.

Phalaenopsis (Orchidaceae) Greenhouse orchids:
amabilis (syn: *P. grandiflora*). Moth Orchid. Flowers to 5 in. (12 cm) across, glistening white, the lip divided into three, the side pieces spotted red and marked yellow, the mid with two long curly tails; in pendent sprays. October to January. Greenhouse. Introduced from Java in 1847 by Thomas Lobb for Veitch.
× *intermedia.* The flower is white, shaded rose-pink and with a small deep purple-pink lip. This, the first natural orchid hybrid to be recognized, was found in 1853 as a solitary plant in a consignment of

PLATE 139
Phygelius capensis at Rattery

P. aphrodite received by Veitch of Exeter from Thomas Lobb. John Seden later raised an identical plant by crossing *P. aphrodite* and *P. rosea*.

Phalaris (Gramineae)
arundinacea 'Woodside' (syn: *P.a.* 'Feesey's Form'). Gardeners' Garters is a grass with leaves lined white and green; invasive, especially in moist soil. About 2 or 3 ft (60–90 cm) high; flower stems to 6 ft (2 m). *P.a.* 'Woodside' has more white in the leaves and is slower growing. A sport at Mervyn Feesey's garden, Woodside, in Barnstaple.

Philesia magellanica (Philesiaceae). See p.86.

Phlox (Polemoniaceae) Rockery Phlox cultivars:

Raised by Harold Bawden, Woodside, West Hill, Ottery St Mary:

Woodside'. A pink flowered seedling of 'Apple Blossom'. May.

Raised at Southcombe Gardens, Widecombe-in-the-Moor:

'Chnodomar'. Vigorous. Narrow-petalled rose-pink flowers from May onwards.

'Gundamund'. Pale lilac flowers May. Large mats.

'Lothaire'. Very pale lilac-pink flowers, rounded, May. Compact.

Phragmipedilum caudatum (Orchidaceae)
See *Cypripedium caudatum*.

Phygelius (Scrophulariaceae)
capensis. Cape Figwort. A partly evergreen shrub with red or orange (occasionally yellow) curved tubular flowers with a yellow mouth, to 1½ in. (3.5 cm) long, in heads to 1½ ft (45 cm) tall, in summer and autumn. Not hardy outside mild areas, though it often succeeds elsewhere grown against a wall, where it usually grows about 5 ft (1.5 m) high but may reach 20 ft (6 m). In hard winters it is likely to be killed down to the ground; a mulch will promote reshooting in the spring. Introduced from South Africa to Veitch and first flowered in the UK at Exeter in 1855.

Physostelma (Asclepiadaceae)
wallichii. A green and yellow flowered shrubby climber, closely allied to *Hoya* and by some experts included in that genus. Collected for Veitch by Thomas Lobb in Singapore in 1847.

Pilgerodendron uviferum (Cupressaceae)
See *Libocedrus uvifera*.

Pimelea (Thymelaeaceae)
suaveolens (syn: *P. macrocephala*). An evergreen shrub to 3 ft (1 m) high, the flowers in domed heads, yellowish in bud, opening pale rose. Greenhouse. Introduced from the Swan River, Western Australia in 1850 by Lucombe, Pince & Co.

Pinus (Pinaceae) Pine
mugo 'The Champ'. An extra dwarf Mountain Pine, growing 2 x 2 in. (5 x 5 cm) in 10 years, raised from seed at Kenwith Castle Nurseries.

PLATE 140
Pleione lagenaria at Burnham Nurseries, Kingsteignton

B. Rittershausen

nigra. Austrian Pine:
'Black Prince'. A bushy plant growing 12–20 in. (30–50 cm) tall in 10 years. Raised by Chantry Nursery from a witch's broom growth.

'Bright Eyes'. Introduced commercially by Chantry Nursery. A dwarf rounded bush, with dark green leaves, named for its white winter buds. Raised from a witch's broom on a tree at Shackleford in Surrey by B. Reynolds in 1972.
radiata 'Isca'. A very slow growing form of the Monterey Pine. The rich emerald-green needles are 5 in. (12 cm) long. An irregular broad pyramid growing about 10 ft (3 m) in 10 years. It is named from the Roman name for Exeter, Isca Dumnoniorum. Found as a chance seedling in the garden of the Imperial Hotel in Exeter by Humphrey Welch, for 30 years the proprietor of The Wansdyke Nursery and The Pygmy Pinetum at Devizes, and author of books on dwarf conifers.
sylvestris. Scots Pine:
'Chantry Blue'. A bushy plant with very blue-grey needles, and candle-like copper-coloured spring growths. Grows about 8 ft (2.5 m) in 10 years and bears cones when young. Found as a witch's broom on a tree on Horsell Common in Surrey by B. Reynolds. Introduced by Don Hatch.

'Jeremy'. It has very short dark green needles, long bright brown buds and grows to about 16 in. (40 cm) high. A dwarf bush found in Wellingborough by B. Reynolds and introduced by Chantry Nursery.

'Kenwith'. A dense green cushion reaching 9 in. (22 cm) high and 12 in. (30 cm) wide in 10 years. Raised at Kenwith Castle Nurseries.

'Lodge Hill'. A slow-growing bush to about 3 ft (1 m) with blue-grey foliage. Propagated from a witch's broom on a tree at Boundstone in Surrey by Chantry Nursery.

Piper (Piperaceae)
porphyrophyllum (syn: *Cissus porphyrophylus* or *C. cordifolius*) Velvet Cissus. A beautiful climbing Pepper with insignificant flowers but with red stems ornamented with lines of white bristles. The large leaves are velvety moss-green with yellow veins and pink specks, and have wine-red undersides. Warm greenhouse. Collected in Malaya by Thomas Lobb for Veitch.

Pitcairnia (Bromeliaceae)
altensteinii gigantea. A large rosette of sword leaves and spikes of whitish flowers with bright red bracts up stems to 7 ft (2 m) tall. From Guyana, then British Guiana; sent by Lucombe, Pince & Co. to Kew Gardens in about 1847. Greenhouse. Sometimes included in the genus *Puya.*

Pittosporum (Pittosporaceae)
tenuifolium. Three cultivars were raised by R. Channon at Plympton in the 1960s. He exported plants to Duncan & Davies nursery in New Zealand in about 1970, from whence they have come into commerce in this country. All have leaves with cream-yellow variegations: 'Marjorie Channon', 'Peggy Dawe' and 'Wendle Channon'.

Platycladus orientalis (Cupressaceae) See *Thuja orientalis*.

Pleione (Orchidaceae). Small orchids growing on mossy rocks and trees in mountain forests with a high rainfall but dry winters. Most need only an unheated greenhouse and some may succeed outside. Introduced to Veitch in 1849 by Thomas Lobb from the Khasia Hills in northern India:

> *humilis.* White flowers, often tinted pale mauve, the lip with rows of red, purple or yellow-brown merging spots. August to May.

> *lagenaria.* Now included in *P. praecox*. Rose-lilac flowers with a whitish lip marked crimson-purple and yellow.

Podocarpus (Podocarpaceae)
> *andinus.* The Plum-fruited Yew. Named from its edible yellow-white fruits, this tree needs shelter from cold winds. A specimen at Bicton Park had grown to 71 ft (22 m) in 1968. Introduced from the Chilean Andes by Richard Pearce in 1860, collecting for the Exeter Veitch Nursery. FCC 1864.
> *nubigenus.* The largest specimen in this country, at Scorrier House, Cornwall, was 45 ft (14 m) high when 50 years old. Introduced from an area of very high rainfall in Chile by William Lobb in 1846, working for the Exeter Veitch Nursery.

Polystichum setiferum (Aspidiaceae)
> 'Kitsonae'. See p.54.
> 'Tripinnatum'. See p.54.

Populus (Salicaceae)
> *candicans* 'Aurora'. This poplar has the second and main flush of leaves much marked with white. It was found in a north Devon garden and first distributed by the now closed Treseders' Nursery of Truro in the 1920s. AM 1954.

PLATE 141
Primula 'Ingram's Blue' at Rosemoor Garden, Great Torrington

Primula (Primulaceae)
> 'Chevithorne Pink'. A vigorous double polyanthus with shell-pink flowers. Although it is stated to be a Devon plant, Dr D.E.C. Nelson has traced its raising to 1950 by Mrs Elison Spence of Stewartstown, Co. Tyrone and later naming by Mrs Emmerson of Limavady, Co. Derry.

> 'Chevithorne Purple'. Fully double rich purple flowers, laced gold. Probably raised at Chevithorne Barton, near Tiverton, in the 1930s.

> 'Craddock Pink'. A primrose with dark glossy green leaves, bronze veined. Scented, large blush-pink flowers with frilled petals and a yellow eye. Found in Miss Marker's garden at Yondercott, near Uffculme, and named by Margery Fish in the 1950s.

> 'Craddock White'. As above but with white flowers.

> *denticulata.* Seeds of the Drumstick Primula were sent from the Himalaya to Veitch of Exeter by John Forbes Royle (1798–1858), Superintendent of the East India Co.'s two hospitals and one botanic garden at Saharanpur, in the Punjab, in north India. It was regarded as tender and first produced its purple globular flower-heads in the UK in 1842 in a Veitch greenhouse.

'Devon Cream'. An oxlip-like plant with heads of nodding creamy yellow flowers. About 1 ft (30 cm) high. Found by Lionel Fortescue at The Garden House, Buckland Monachorum. (There is also an auricula bearing this name.)

'Harry Adams'. See 87.

'Ingram's Blue'. Collingwood Ingram bred and selected seedlings, aiming to reduce the yellow eye in blue primulas. The results, with deep violet-blue polyanthus-type flowers and only small yellow eyes, were named and introduced by the Lady Anne Palmer of Rosemoor.
vulgaris. Wild Primrose:
'Large Sulphur'. A primrose found in a wood in Devon, with neat large fully double flowers. It was listed by Glazeley Gardens, Bridgnorth, Shropshire.

'Pridhamsleigh'. See p.88.

Primroses and polyanthus raised at E.B. Champernowne's nursery at Green Lane Gardens, Buckland Monachorum, around 1950.
'Afterglow'. A juliana hybrid (similar to 'Wanda') with rich orange-red flowers over a long period.

'Anita'. Large plum-purple primrose flowers, so numerous as to hide the leaves.

'Blue Cockade'. Violet-blue flowers with orange-yellow eye. Dwarf polyanthus.

'Buckland Belle'. A vigorous plant with violet-blue flowers that have large pale yellow centres. A juliana hybrid introduced in 1952.

'Buckland Cream'. Garryarde hybrid.

'Buckland Enchantress'.

'Buckland Primrose'. A vigorous dwarf polyanthus with very large primrose-yellow flowers and bronzy-green foliage.

'Buckland Scarlet'.

'Buckland Wine'. See p.87.

'Buff Pink'. Hose-in-hose primrose flowers.

'Crimson Glory'. Immense blooms of clear crimson, deepening with age. Primrose.

'Czar'. Flowers the colour of Czar Plums: matt bluey-red. Dwarf polyanthus.

'David Green'. Intense crimson, deep yellow eye. Primrose.

'Emperor'. Very large rounded wine-purple flowers. Primrose.

'Hunter's Moon'. Old-gold polyanthus flowers with rich yellow eye; 6 in. (15 cm).

'Jeffrey's Strain'. Primrose, including crimson, pink, buff and violet but no whites or yellows, raised by Mr Jeffrey, who had worked at Dartington Hall. He probably raised many of the other Champernowne Primulas.

'Joan Schofield'. Large clear ruby-red with deep yellow eye, from early March to late May. Primrose.

'Light Red'. Hose-in-hose primrose.

'Martin Argles'. Deep 'Wanda' purple, the bright yellow eye edged crimson. Primrose.

'Pauline'. Large deep orange-rose flowers. Primrose.

'Pink Beauty'. Hose-in-hose primrose.

'Raspberries and Cream'. Deep raspberry-coloured flowers, edged cream. Dwarf polyanthus.

'Red Ensign'. Flowers velvety crimson that shades into the very large deep yellow centre. 4 in. (10 cm) Polyanthus.

'Sunset Glow'. Fiery orange-scarlet, needing shade to keep the flower colour. Primrose.

'Tiny Tim'. A very small 'Wanda'-type plant with tiny bright cherry-red flowers.

'Veronica'. Speedwell-blue primrose.

'Wanda's Rival'. Very many clear rose-lilac flowers in spring and autumn.
As well as the hose-in-hose primroses listed, Champernowne developed their own strain of vigorous hose-in-hose polyanthus with each set of petals of equal size, and sometimes of differing colours such as pink and carmine, or purple and rose.

They also raised their own strain of Jack-in-the-Green, with white, yellow, pink, crimson or purple flowers, each set on a bed of leaves that are much larger than those of Tudor times.

Proustia pyrifolia (Compositae). A greenhouse climber with small spines, and large dense heads of both pale lilac flowers and of seeds with purple dandelion-clocks. Introduced from Chile in 1862 by Pearce for Veitch of Exeter.

Prunus (Rosaceae)
avium. Wild Cherry or Mazzard. Cultivars were formerly grown for fruit in Devon, especially for markets. Those known in 1924 had small black fruits with very dark red flesh: 'Dun', 'Large Black', 'Preserving' and 'Small Black'. 'Dun', 'Small Dun', 'Green-stemmed Black' and 'Bottlers' were once stocked by Westacott Nurseries near Barnstaple.
domestica. Plum:
'Dittisham Plum'. See p.89.
'Lucombe's Nonesuch', now probably extinct, was raised at Lucombe's Exeter nursery early in the last century.
persica. Peach:
'Dymond' was introduced by Veitch of Exeter in 19th century and named after the raiser; probably the nurseryman who exhibited in Exeter in 1832.
'Late Devonian' raised by Robert Veitch & Son in 1894.

Pteris (Pteridaceae)
argyraea. A tropical fern with large fronds with light green segments coloured white down their middles. Introduced from central India by Thomas Lobb collecting for Veitch of Exeter.

Pterodiscus (Pedaliaceae)
speciosus. A dwarf herbaceous plant, growing from a rootstock that pokes above ground, with purple-rose petunia-like flowers. Greenhouse. Introduced from South Africa by Veitch in 1845 or before.

Pulmonaria (Boraginaceae)
'Weetwood'. A very deep blue hybrid of *P. longifolia* selected by Harold Bawden.

Puya altensteinii gigantea (Bromeliaceae). See *Pitcairnia*.

Pyrus (Rosaceae) Pear
cordata. The Plymouth or Lesser Pear is found on the western edge of Europe. It was first described from the wild in England in 1865 and it is now restricted to a few hedgerows on the outskirts of Plymouth. A shrub or tree to 25 ft (8 m) tall, usually spiny; with white flowers, striped pink outside, sweetly scented at night, usually in late May. The fruit is small and inedible.

PLATE 142
Pyrus cordata 'Plymouth Pear' at Estover, Plymouth

In 1834 the Rev. John Huyshe of Clyst Hydon crossed 'Marie Louise' and 'Gansel's Bergamot' and from the 3 pips that ripened he raised:

'Prince of Wales', originally called 'Huyshe's Bergamot' from the flavour of the fruit. A poor cropper needing a sheltered site.

'Princess of Wales'. A delicate plant with well-flavoured fruit.

'Victoria'. A hardy and prolific pear with frost-resistant flowers.

They were marketed by Lucombe, Pince & Co.

Huyshe also raised, before 1864, a seedling of 'Beurre d'Aremberg' called:

'Prince Consort'. The fruit is "very juicy, sweet and vinous with a powerful and peculiar flavour unlike any other Pear". (*The Herefordshire Pomona*). His cultivar names are sometimes prefixed 'Huyshe's'.

Quercus (Fagaceae) Oak
× *hispanica*
'Lucombeana'. See p.90.
'Crispa'. See p.90.
'Dentata'. See p.91.
'Heterophylla'. See p.91.
'Suberosa'. See p.91.
ilex. Holm or Evergreen Oak.
'Bicton' Large wide leaves. Found in Bicton Gardens, and distributed by Hilliers Nurseries. It may be identical with 'Rotundifolia'.
'Fordii'. This Holm Oak has narrow leaves, very dark green. The only mature plant known is in the Royal Botanic Gardens, Edinburgh, although Killerton had a young specimen. Raised in Lucombe & Pince's nursery before 1843.

Rhaphithamnus (Verbenaceae)
spinosus. Pale blue flowers and bright blue berries on a spiny evergreen shrub or small tree, that needs a sheltered spot. Introduced from Chile by William Lobb to Veitch of Exeter in about 1843.

Rhododendron (Ericaceae)

Species
augustinii 'Dartington Blue'. Usually 4 to 10 ft (1.35–3 m) high, the flowers varying from white to pink to purple-blue. *R.* 'Dartington Blue' is a good blue form selected at Dartington Hall in the 1930s.
brookeanum. A straggling evergreen bush, usually growing on trees. The leaves are up to 10 in. (25 cm) long. The flowers, about 3 in. (7.5 cm) long, are orange, sometimes pure, sometimes mixed with pink, yellow or red. Pale yellow forms were also found by Thomas Lobb, who introduced plants from Mt Kinabalu, Sarawak, for Veitch who first flowered it in 1855. It was named after Sir James Brooke, Rajah of Sarawak.
glaucophyllum. 'Len Beer'. See p.94.
jasminiflorum. Jasmine-like flowers with straight tubes about 2 in. (5 cm) long and flared wavy petals; white or sometimes pinkish, with the anthers forming a deep pink eye, in heads of up to 20. May to September. Warm greenhouse. Collected on Mt Ophir, Malacca, by Thomas Lobb for Veitch in 1848.
javanicum. Up to 6 ft (2 m) high, with handsome dark glossy green foliage, scaly on the underside; there are various coloured forms, with trusses 6 in. (15 cm) wide. Thomas Lobb introduced a rich orange-yellow form, with dark purple anthers, from Java, for Veitch, who first flowered it in 1847. Warm greenhouse. With the preceding species, this forms a parent of a range of greenhouse rhododendrons known as javanico-jasminiflorum hybrids.
kaempferi. An evergreen of the azalea series, with white to red flowers in May and June, growing to 10 ft (3 m) high. Veitch of Exeter raised two later-flowering forms, which are best grown in light shade to preserve the flower colours:
'Daimio' Salmon-pink.
'Mikado' Pale apricot-salmon (not to

PLATE 143
Rhododendron augustinii 'Dartington Blue' at Dartington

be confused with the Aberconway hybrid of the same name).

lobbii. Bright scarlet tubular flowers, in trusses of from 8–12 blooms. Introduced from Borneo by Thomas Lobb, 1861.

macrophyllum. Compact trusses of up to 20 or more rose-purple to pink bell-shaped flowers, with reddish-brown spots. May and June. A hardy 12 ft (4 m) evergreen, introduced from California in 1850 by William Lobb, collecting for Veitch of Exeter.

malayanum. A compact plant with small cerise-crimson nodding flowers. Introduced from Mt Ophir, Malacca, by Thomas Lobb for Veitch, 1854.

occidentale. See p.91.

veitchianum. A greenhouse shrub with fragrant large white flowers, slightly greenish outside, cut and often crinkled. Introduced from Moulmein by Thomas Lobb, and first flowered by Veitch of Exeter in 1857.

Hybrids

Endsleigh, Milton Abbot

'Endsleigh Pink'. Dark matt-green leaves with bronze undersides. Clear pink flowers. 20 x 15 ft (6 x 5 m). A *R. arboreum* hybrid from the then estate of the Dukes of Bedford.

Lionel Fortescue, The Garden House, Buckland Monachorum

'Buckland' ('Vanessa Pastel' × *R. yakushimanum*). Clear pink. AM 1985.

'Buckland Beauty' (*R. griffithianum* × 'Letty Edwards'). White with faint green eye. Mid-season.

'Buckland Cream' ('Windsor Hawk' × *R. loderi* 'Julie'). Creamy-yellow. Mid season.

'Cecily Fortescue' (*R. yakushimanum* × 'Hawk'). White, lightly spotted red at base. Late-flowering.

'Katharine Fortescue'. See p.94.

'Lionel Fortescue' ('Hawk' × *R. wardii* 'Ellestree'). Yellow with red eye. Mid-season.

'Nancy Fortescue' (*R. concatenans* × 'Lady Alice Fitzwilliam'). Grey-blue leaves. Dusky orange bell-flowers. Early to mid-season.

'William Fortescue' (*R. griffithianum* × *R. campylocarpum elatum*). Pink buds, opening to cream, fading to nearly white. Early.

(More crosses are yet to be registered.)

PLATE 144
Rhododendron 'Endsleigh Pink' at Bickham House, near Yelverton

Terry Jones, Zeal Monachorum
'Zeal Doubloon'. See p.95.
Lucombe, Pince, Co., Exeter
'Purpureum Grandiflorum'. Large
heads of rather pale violet-purple
flowers. An undated catalogue of
Lucombe, Pince & Co., probably from
the middle of the last century, claims
that this cv. was raised by Pince, though
it is usually credited to Hosea Waterer
(1793–1853) of Knap Hill Nursery,
Surrey. Lucombe, Pince & Co. listed
28 other rhododendron hybrids of their
own raising, which are probably all
extinct.
Thomas Luscombe, Lower Coombe
Royal, Kingsbridge
'Coombe Royal'. See p.94.

'Frances Thiselton-Dyer'. ($\times$ *R.
fortunei*.) Bright rosy-red flowers with a
large maroon blotch in the throat.
Raised by T. Luscombe and first
flowered at Kew Gardens in 1896.

'Luscombei'. See p. 94.

'Luscombei Splendens'. Rich blood-
crimson flowers, otherwise similar to *R.*
'Luscombei'. A *R. fortunei* $\times$ *R.
thomsonii* cross raised by Luscombe in
about 1880.

'Mrs W.T. Thiselton-Dyer'. Each
flower is nearly 4 in. (10 cm) across,
rose-pink with a maroon blotch in the
throat. A *R. thomsonii* hybrid, raised by
Luscombe, and planted at Kew, where
it first flowered in 1896. It was named
after the wife of the Director.

'Elisabeth Lock'. Silvery-pink flowers,
deeper outside, 3 in. (7.5 cm) across, in
trusses. Very late. A hybrid of *R.
auriculatum* found in the garden at
Lower Coombe Royal, and named by
the then owner, Surgeon-Capt.
J.A.N.Lock, R.N. AM 1968.
Greenway House, Galmpton
'Greenway'. An evergreen azalea with

brilliant flame-coloured flowers, found
at Greenway and named by Charles
Williams. AM 1975.
The Lady Anne Palmer, Rosemoor,
Torrington
trichostomum 'Collingwood Ingram'. A
small aromatic twiggy shrub with
bright pink daphne-like flowers in May
and June. A seedling raised by
Glendoick Gardens Ltd from
Edinburgh Royal Botanic Garden seed;
selected, named and introduced by the
Lady Anne Palmer. FCC 1976.
Veitch's Nurseries, Exeter
caucasicum albiflorum (so-called). A low-
growing plant with white flowers,
spotted with yellow. Raised by Veitch
in 1840, from crossing *R. caucasicum*
with *R. luteum album*.
'Exminster'. Large cream bell-flowers,
heavily flushed with pink. Raised at
Penjerrick in Cornwall by Barclay Fox
from crossing *R. campylocarpum* and *R.
thomsonii*. It was put into commerce by
Robert Veitch & Son, who named it
after their Exminster nursery.

'Exoniense'. A cross between *R. ciliatum*
and *R. veitchianum* raised at Robert
Veitch & Son, Exeter, in 1881.

'Princess of Orange'. A hybrid of *R.
campylocarpum* and *R.* 'Prince Camille
de Rohan' raised by Robert Veitch &
Son at Exeter in about 1907.

Ribes (Grossulariaceae)
lobbii. A 3–6 ft (1–2 m) high spiny shrub
with purplish-red and white fuchsia-like
flowers in April, and small red-brown
gooseberries, introduced from N.
California in 1852 by William Lobb for
Veitch.
nigrum. Black currant. 'Coronation' was
raised by George Pyne, Denver Nurseries,
Topsham.

'Pyne's Upright'. This Red currant was

raised by George Pyne. It had large sweet dark red fruit.

uva-crispa. Gooseberry. 'May Duke'. Dark red fruit, with an excellent flavour after cooking. It was for many years the main gooseberry grown in the Tamar valley for early fruit. It was still much grown there, and at Cheddar and in the Exe area in 1945. Raised by George Pyne, introduced in 1900. He also raised 'Denver Red'.

Robinia (Leguminosae)

hispida. The Rose Acacia is a suckering shrub with deep rose-pink pea-flowers, many leaflets and very brittle branches; usually produced as a graft on *R. pseudacacia.* It was introduced from South-eastern U.S.A. in 1743 by Sir John Colleton of Exmouth.

Rosa (Rosaceae) Rose

'Angela Rippon'. Large, full, coral-pink flowers on a bushy plant. Named after the Devon broadcaster. This miniature rose was raised at the nursery of G. de Ruitar in Holland in 1978.

'Devoniensis' and 'Climbing Devoniensis'. See p.95.

'Edward Hyams'. 2½ in. (6 cm) deep orange-yellow flowers with a reddish blotch at the base of each petal, and greyish-green leaves with usually 7 leaflets. Found in Edward Hyams' garden at Hill House, Landscove. He had raised it from plants or seed which he brought back from semi-desert hills near Shahrud, in north Iran, in 1972. It is probably a hybrid between *R. persica,* which has one leaflet and red-blotched flowers, and another species, perhaps *R. bungeana. R. persica* is sometimes known as *Hulthemia persica,* and its hybrids with other roses as × *Hulthemosa.*

Roses raised by Edgar M. Allen CMG (1883–1968). After many years as a shipping agent in Suez, Edgar Allen retired to Bideford in 1945 where he continued a lifetime interest in growing roses, a successful exhibitor, twice winning the National Rose Society's Amateur Championship. With failing health he turned in 1957 to breeding, and the following of his roses were awarded Certificates of Merit at the National Rose Society trial grounds. He first suggested the Rose of Torridge Competition for Amateur rose hybridists and donated the annual prizes. At Bath University he sponsored research on roses:

'Eve Allen'. Named after his wife. A hybrid tea with flowers to 4 in. (10 cm) across, cherry and old-gold, sweetly scented.

'Westward Ho!' Upper leaves copper-beech coloured. Hybrid tea flowers to 4½ in. (11 cm) across, scarlet with a silver reverse. Scored 5 out of 10 for fragrance.

Roses bred by J. Pearce at The Limes New Roses, Lifton (wholesale):

'Arthur Bell': 1979; deep yellow; climbing 10–15 ft (3–4.5 m).

'Bush Baby': 1986; pale pink; 6 in. (15 cm).

'Dame Vera Lynn': 1988; salmon and brick clustered flowers. 2 ft (60 cm).

'Dr McAlpine': 1983; rose-pink; 15 in. (35 cm).

'Geraldine': 1984; orange hybrid tea; 2–3 ft (60–90 cm).

'Gilda': 1989; shell-pink; 2½–4 ft (75–120 cm).

'Jane Asher': 1988; bright scarlet; 10–14 in. (25–35 cm).

'Leaping Salmon': Salmon; climbing 6–10 ft (2–3 m).

'Ragtime': apricot-pink floribunda; 8 in. (45 cm).

Christopher Warner, a schoolteacher who lived at Liverton, near Newton Abbot, had a small rose nursery, and bred the following plants. He has since moved to Shropshire and is pursuing rose growing full-time. Author of *Climbing Roses* published by Century in 1987.

'Chew Legacy' ('Edith Holden'): a tall cluster-flowered rose of a new colour – tan-brown. Introduced by E.B. Le Grice & Co.

'Chewarvel': a yellow climbing miniature, due for introduction in 1990. Silver Medal at Baden Baden International Trials 1988.

'Chewizz': a vermilion climbing miniature, again due for introduction in 1990. Trial Ground Certificate at The Royal National Rose Society's gardens in St Albans.

'Devon Maid': fragrant pink flowers; climbing 8–10 ft (2.5–3 m).

'Iris Webb': named after the founder and first Chairman of the NCCPG (Devon Group), famous in the flower-arranging world; a compact bush with clustered flowers of tan-brown and gold; likely to be introduced in 1990.

'Liverton Lady': pink flowers; climbing 15–20 ft (4.5–6 m); will cover the side of a house.

'Pillarbox': a vivid vermilion cluster-flowered rose. Selected by the Post Office as its official rose.

M. Russell

PLATE 145
Rosmarinus 'Primley Blue' at Hoggetts, Zeal Monachorum

Rosa 'Weetwood'. See p.96.

Rosmarinus (Labiatae) Rosemary
officinalis 'Primley Blue'. A dense evergreen aromatic bush 3–4 ft (1–1.25 m) high and 6 ft (2 m) wide. Rich mid-blue flowers in mild spells from late September until April, and then very freely in the spring. Raised at Herbert Whitley's Primley Botanic Nursery.

Roupellia grata (Apocynaceae). See *Strophanthus gratus*.

Rubus (Rosaceae)
'Better-Late' was raised by George Pyne of Denver Nurseries, Topsham, in about 1931 by crossing a red-fruiting hybrid berry with a raspberry.

'Betty Ashburner'. An evergreen thornless carpeter, with transparent orange fruits, lower and less rampant than *Rubus tricolor*, of which it is a chance seedling crossed with *R. calycinoides*, raised by Kenneth Ashburner, Stone Lane Gardens, near Chagford.

'Denver Thornless'. A blackberry raised by George Pyne before 1949.

'Hildaberry'. See p.96.
idaeus Raspberry
George Pyne raised:
　'Condor'.

　'Devon' ('The Devon') in 1900, with pale red berries, sweet and late.

　'Heytor'. [*sic*]. Introduced by Pyne in 1915.

　'Mayfair', about 1929, a seedling of 'Pyne's Park Lane'.

　'Pyne's Imperial', introduced in 1928, a seedling of 'Pyne's Royal' with similar but larger fruit.

　'Pyne's Park Lane', about 1912, had round bright red fruit with a very good flavour.

'Pyne's Red Cross', introduced in 1917, with roundish light red fruit.

'Pyne's Royal', raised 1907, and introduced 6 years later; with large conical dark red fruit. It was one of the parents of the early Malling varieties raised by Norman Grubb. By 1935 it had deteriorated, probably from virus infection.
Robert Veitch & Son raised 'Exeter Yellow'.

'Kenneth Ashburner'. Good thornless evergreen cover for a bank, usually producing edible blackberries, especially if grown near a parent. Raised from crossing the scrambling, narrow-lobed *Rubus henryi* with the invasive *R. tricolor*, by K. Ashburner.

Ruellia (Acanthaceae)
spectabilis. A hot-house annual or perennial herbaceous plant with 3½ in. (8.5 cm) long trumpet flowers, purplish-blue with dark veins, needing a fertile light soil. Introduced in 1849 from Peru by William Lobb for Veitch.

Sanchezia (Acanthaceae). Handsome greenhouse undershrubs with tubular flowers, from Ecuador, introduced by Pearce for Veitch in 1863.
longiflora. Hanging purple flower trusses in April.
nobilis. Clusters of erect yellow flowers in bright red leaf-like bracts, on purple stems, in June.

Saxegothaea (Podocarpaceae)
conspicua. Prince Albert's Yew (the genus was named in his honour). A very slow-growing tree native to the forests of central Chile and adjacent Argentina. Introduced by William Lobb in 1846 for the Exeter Veitch nursery.

Saxifraga (Saxifragaceae)
'Dartington Double'. See p.97.

'Devon Ghost'. A mossy saxifrage variegated with grey and cream, forming smooth cushions with white flowers. A sport of 'Pearly King' at Lin and Ray Brown's Torbay's Plant World, St Marychurch Road, Newton Abbot, in 1987.

'Four Winds'. Mossy carpets. Large dark red flowers with whitish centres. May. Raised at the now closed Four Winds Nursery, Georgeham.

Schizostylis (Iridaceae) Kaffir Lily.
coccinea 'Tambara'. An early flowering form; the rose-pink flowers with lighter outsides, produced from late July, instead of from the usual September or October; collected as seed near the tops of mountains on the borders of Zimbabwe (then Rhodesia) and Mozambique and distributed by Lady Drewe of Broadhembury House, near Honiton, in 1956.

'Zeal Salmon'. See p.97.

Schlumbergera (Cactaceae). In the Organ Mountains of Brazil, this genus grows on trees in forests. The Christmas Cactus was raised by crossing two of the species. Fleshy arching to hanging stems, smooth, flattened and jointed. Tubular flowers with protruding stamens. Greenhouse. The cultivars listed below were raised by the late W.B. Tobey of Chillington, near Kingsbridge:
'Burton Tobey': Flowers 3 in. (7.5 cm) long and nearly as wide, white lightly flushed red-purple at the base, and edged red-purple. From November. FCC 1976.

'Ilona': Flowers 2½ in. (6 cm) long, silvery white, the upper half lightly flushed red-purple that darkens towards the edges and tips. From November. AM 1976.

Scilla hispanica 'Chevithorne' (Liliaceae) See *Hyacinthoides* p.

Scindapsus (Araceae)
pictus. Silver Vine. Climbing ivy-like to 40 ft (12 m). The leaves are dark green with silvery, pale green spots and clouds. Arum (Lords and Ladies) flowers with white hoods. Greenhouse. Introduced from Malaya by Thomas Lobb for Veitch.

Selaginella (Selaginaceae). Resembling mosses and allied to the Club-mosses. Thomas Lobb, working for Veitch of Exeter, introduced the following from Borneo:
atroviridis. Bright green, a few in. high.
griffithii. To 1 ft (30 cm) high.
lobbii. A giant with running stems to 4 ft (120 cm) long.

Senecio cruentus (Compositae). See *Cineraria.*

Sequoiadendron giganteum (Taxodiaceae) See p.97.

Silene (Caryophyllaceae).
vulgaris maritima 'Flore Pleno'. The double Sea Campion was found in the wild in Devon over 100 years ago.

PLATE 146
Sonerila margaritacea argentea

Sinningia (Gesneriaceae)
speciosa macrophylla. Large hairy leaves with white veins. Rather bell-shaped flared flowers, usually pale lavender. Introduced in 1842 from Brazil by William Lobb for Veitch. Often, but wrongly, called *Gloxinia;* the modern flowers of that name are mostly derived from the type *Sinningia speciosa,* introduced in 1815.

Sisyrinchium striatum 'Aunt May' (Iridaceae). See p.98.

Smithiantha (Gesneriaceae)
'Exoniensis'. Temple Bells. A showy hot-house perennial with a red velvet sheen on the leaves and, in the winter, large bunches of tubular, deep orange-scarlet flowers with yellow throats. Raised by R.T. Pince of Lucombe, Pince & Co. in about 1869 from crossing *S.* 'Refulgens' with *S. zebrina.* Often labelled *Gesneria* or *Naegelia.*

Solandra (Solanaceae)
longiflora laevis. Trumpet Plant. From Jamaica. A 6 ft (2 m) shrub with fragrant trumpet flowers about 1 ft (30 cm) long, greenish-cream, white at the mouth. November. Warm greenhouse. Flowered by Lucombe, Pince & Co. in 1848.

Sonerila (Melastomataceae). Small shrubs or herbaceous plants with flower parts in threes. Shade in a warm moist greenhouse. Introduced to Veitch by Thomas Lobb:
margaritacea. Pearly Margaritacea. Scarlet trailing stems to 10 in. (25 cm) long. Shining copper-green leaves with pearl-white spots and bristles that in sunlight look like frost; the undersides pink with red-purple veins. Rose-pink flowers with prominent yellow anthers. Java. 1854.
speciosa (syn: *elegans*). To 1 ft (30 cm) high. Showy mauve flowers. 1856.

stricta. About 6 in. (15 cm) high, a downy plant with small purplish-pink flowers. 1848. Java.

Sorbus devoniensis (Rosaceae). See p.99.

Spathoglottis (Orchidaceae)
aurea. Deep yellow flowers with a few crimson spots on the lip, to 3 in. (7.5 cm) across, on 2–3 ft (60–90 cm) stems. Warm greenhouse. A Malaysian Orchid collected on Mt Ophir in 1840, by Thomas Lobb for Veitch.

Spiraea (Rosaceae)
densiflora. Less than 2 ft (60 cm) high, with rose-pink flowers in many domes to 1½ in. (3.5 cm) across in June. Growing in Veitch's Exeter nursery in 1861 and probably introduced from Oregon by William Lobb. Probably not in cultivation.

Spraguea (Portulacaceae)
umbellata (syn: *Calyptridium umbellatum*). Pussy Paws is a half-hardy perennial (sometimes annual), related to *Lewisia.* Rosettes of small fleshy leaves. Tiny flowers in woolly pinkish heads in July. Found among mountain stones in the wild. Introduced from California to Veitch by William Lobb and first flowered at Exeter in 1859.

Stachyurus (Stachyuraceae)
praecox 'Devon Purple'. An unusual purple-leafed form of *Stachyurus praecox* discovered in an East Budleigh garden in the 1970s. Like the species, it is a deciduous shrub up to 10 ft (3 m) tall, with pale yellow flowers, in February to March, borne in stiff drooping racemes about 3 in. (7.5 cm) long. The shrub is vigorous and hardy. Japan.

Stenoloma (Polypodiaceae)
chusanum veitchiana. A tropical fern with creeping rhizomes and feathery fronds to 15 x 9 in. (35 x 22 cm). Sent to Exeter from

PLATE 147
Streptosolen jamesonii at Ness Gardens, University of Liverpool

Malaya in the early 1840s, it was the only plant introduced by John Veitch, a naval surgeon, despite his father James's high hopes.

Stigmaphyllon (Malpighiaceae).
heterophyllum. A large greenhouse climber with roundish frilled leaves and, in December, yellow flowers with curious and attractive stalked, frilly petals. Introduced from Argentina in 1842 by William Lobb for Veitch.

Streptocarpus michelmorei (Gesneriaceae) See p.99.

Streptosolen (Solanaceae).
jamesonii (syn: *Browallia jamesonii*). Marmalade Bush. A hairy evergreen shrub, scrambling 6 or 8 ft (2–2.5 m), with 1¼ in. (3 cm) long funnel-shaped orange flowers in dense rounded clusters from May to July. Greenhouse. Introduced by William Lobb to Veitch from Colombia in 1847.

Strophanthus (Apocynaceae).
gratus (syn: *Roupellia grata*). Climbing Oleander or Creamfruit. Climbing, with leaves about 6 in. (15 cm) long and heads of fragrant pale pink flowers, flushed

purplish-red outside, the centres ringed in rich pink, the petals long and twisted. Warm greenhouse. Sent from Sierra Leone by Mr Whitfield to Mrs Halford, Newcourt, near Exeter, in the last century. Now cultivated in most tropical countries.

Stylidium (Stylidiaceae)
dichotomum (syn: *S. mucronifolium*). A Trigger Plant with needle leaves and spires of yellow flowers. Each flower has a central finger that springs up when its base is touched, to deposit or receive pollen from visiting insects. Introduced by Lucombe, Pince & Co. from the Swan River area of Australia in 1850.

Tabernaemontana (Apocynaceae)
longiflora. An evergreen tree with large flat white flowers on very long tubes, clover-scented, in the summer. Warm greenhouse. Introduced from Sierra Leone by Lucombe, Pince & Co. in 1849.

Tacsonia (Passifloraceae). See *Passiflora.*

Taxus (Taxaceae)
baccata 'Corley's Coppertip'. A dense spreading bush, to 2 ft (60 cm) high if staked, with bright copper young growths. Raised by the late Ron Corley of High Wycombe from crossing *T.b* 'Dovastonii Aurea' and *T.b.* 'Adpressa Variegata'. Introduced by Chantry Nurseries.

PLATE 148
Thujopsis dolobrata

Sri Kartowieda

Thibaudia macrantha (Ericaceae). See *Agapetes incurvata macrantha.*

Thottea (Aristolochiaceae)
dependens. A 3 ft (1 m) high forest shrub introduced from Malaya by Thomas Lobb for Veitch. Previously included in *Lobbia.*

Thuja (Cupressaceae)
orientalis 'Kenwith'. A dwarf Chinese *thuja* with yellow outer foliage. The inner foliage is green, turning purple in the winter. Raised at Kenwith Castle Nurseries.
plicata. Western Red Cedar. Narrow and erect until quite old, it can reach over 130 ft (40 m) high in this country, though is equally happy as a clipped hedge. Introduced from Oregon in west USA by William Lobb for Veitch of Exeter in 1853.

Thujopsis (Cupressaceae)
dolabrata. A tree, rather similar to Western Red Cedar. First introduced in 1853 from the Buitenzorg Botanic Garden in Java by Thomas Lobb; a single specimen, which died before being propagated, was sent to Veitch's Exeter nursery. In 1859 Captain Fortescue brought a plant from its native Japan for his garden at Castle Hill, Devon. This was successfully reproduced. FCC 1864.

Thymus (Labiatae). Thyme cultivars raised at Southcombe Gardens, Widecombe-in-the-Moor, tolerating winter wet:
'Southcombe Spreader'. Invasive mats. Bright mauve-pink flowers. June-July.
'Widecombe'. Hairy dark green mats, lemon scented. Leaves flecked yellow, especially new growths. Bluey-purple flowers. Summer.

Tibouchina (Melastomataceae)
elegans. A weak evergreen 5 ft (1.5 m) shrub, with abundant showy 2 in. (5 cm) purple flowers with handsome stamens. Warm greenhouse. Introduced from

Brazil in 1846 by William Lobb for
Veitch.

Torreya (Taxaceae)
californica. The California Nutmeg has
needles to 3 in. (7.5 cm) long, plum-like
fruits, horizontal branches in whorls, and
can grow to 70 ft (22 m) in the UK
Discovered and introduced by William
Lobb for Veitch of Exeter in 1851.

PLATE 149
Torreya californica

Trichantha (Gesneriaceae)
minor. A woody climber with one leaf of
each pair very small, and 2 in. (5 cm) long
dark purple flowers with yellow mouths.
Warm greenhouse. Introduced as a
specimen from Colombia by William
Lobb and as seed from Ecuador by
Richard Pearce, for Veitch, who first
flowered it in 1863.

Trichomanes (Hymenophyllaceae)
pluma. A tropical fern with small delicate
feathery fronds introduced from Sarawak
by Thomas Lobb for Veitch of Exeter.

Tricuspidaria lanceolata (Elaeocarpaceae)
See *Crinodendron hookerianum.*

Tropaeolum (Tropaeolaceae). Relatives of
the garden nasturtium, the following species
were introduced to Veitch by William Lobb
from South America:

azureum. See p.102.
crenatiflorum. Pale orange blooms,
somewhat lined red. Annual and tender.
Peru. 1845.
peltophorum (syn: *T. lobbianum*). The
flowers, to 1 in. (2.5 cm) across, are bright
orange-red, or occasionally yellow. A fast-
growing annual. Colombia. 1843.
speciosum. See p.102.
umbellatum. Flowers 1¼ in. (3 cm) long,
scarlet with yellow sepals, in clusters, from
June. A strongly growing perennial with
large tubers. Greenhouse. Bolivia. 1847.

Ulex (Leguminosae)
europaeus 'Flore Pleno'. More compact
than the wild plant, with longer-lasting
flowers, and being sterile, it is useful where
seedlings would be a nuisance. AGM 1929,
AM 1967. Although Bean says that the
Double-flowered Gorse first appeared in
the nursery of John Miller of Bristol in
1828. Loudon states that it was first found
in Devon in about 1825.

Ulmus (Ulmaceae)
glabra 'Exoniensis' (syn: *U.g.* 'Fastigiata').
The Exeter Elm is an erect form of the
Wych Elm; narrow when young, broader
later. The twisted dark green leaves are in
clusters. Found at William Ford's Hill's
Court Nursery, Longbrooke St, Exeter
before 1826. There are two young plants
in the grounds of County Hall, Exeter.

PLATE 150
Ulmus glabra 'Exoniensis' at County Hall, Exeter

161

PLATE 151
Vanda caerulea

Vaccinium (Ericaceae).
'June Ashburner'. A 3–4 ft (1–1.25 m) high evergreen with coppery-red young shoots, small shining leaves, small white bell flowers, and large fruit, edible and good for sauce and jam. It needs an acid soil and a cool root run. A hybrid of the Box Blueberry, *Vaccinium ovatum*, crossed with *V. floribundum*, raised by Kenneth Ashburner of Stone Lane Gardens near Chagford, and named after his wife.
leucostomum. Flowers scarlet tipped with white. A greenhouse shrub needing an acid soil. Raised by Veitch in 1848 from seed collected by William Lobb in Peru.

Vanda (Orchidaceae). Two evergreen greenhouse orchids introduced to Veitch by Thomas Lobb. In the wild they are mostly found perched in the tops of trees in rain-forests:
caerulea. The Blue Orchid. Flowers to 5 in. (12 cm) across, pale violet-blue, usually chequered with a deeper blue, sweetly scented, up to 20 on each 2 to 3 ft (60–90 cm) stem. Autumn. Assam. 1849.
tricolor suavis. Waxy-white flowers, dotted blood-purple, with a deep rose-purple lip; clove-scented; more than 3 in. (7.5 cm) across. Java.

Viola (Violaceae) Violet, Pansy and Viola 'Beaton's Good-Gracious Double Bedding Pansy', an old cv., from Devon rediscovered in 1862 by Donald Beaton, and distributed by James Carter & Co. of High Holborn, London. It had fully double purple flowers. The name upset the naturalist P.H. Gosse, then of St Marychurch, Torquay who thought "Good-Gracious" equivalent to "Good God" and near to blasphemy. FCC 1862.

Violas raised or introduced by Miss E.A. (Nellie) Britton, Washfield Nursery, near Tiverton. The nursery traded from about the 1930s to the 1950s:
'Black Knight'. A cross betewen *V. gracilis* and *V.* 'Bowles Black'. Dense black blooms overlaid with a silky sheen, and with a hint of purple round the golden eye, 1936.

'Chevithorne'. Neat primrose-yellow flowers.

'Nellie Britton'. Small pale lilac-pink flowers on upright plants about 4 in. (10 cm) high. Also known as *V.* 'Haslemere'.

cornuta 'Dr Smart'. Blue-mauve flower with a cream eye, deep navy-blue veining and a paler reverse, moderately scented. Floriferous. Collected by Dr Smart of Marwood in Spain recently.

'Dartington Blue'. See p.103.

odorata. Cultivars or hybrids of the Sweet Violet, with fragrant flowers from early spring to summer, forming mats about 4 in. (10 cm) high. (See also p.103).
'Devonia'. Large reddish-mauve flowers, very sweet scented and vigorous. Introduced by J. Heath of Kingskerswell in 1905.

'Lady Clifford'. Giant purple-blue flowers with a white eye. Raised at Ugbrooke Park, the seat of the Cliffords, near Chudleigh, in 1903.

'Mother's Day'. White flowers with an indefinite mauve-blue eye. Raised by the late Mary Mottram, Yardewell Cross, near South Molton.

'Northcourt'. Rose-pink with a pale mauve centre. Raised in 1911, perhaps in Torquay. Probably extinct.

'Thomas'. Lilac-mauve flowers, very similar to *V.o.* 'Norah Church'. Raised by Mary Mottram.

PLATE 152
Viola cornuta 'Dr Smart' at Marwood Hill, near Barnstaple

Raised or introduced by Windward Violet Farm, Dawlish. Founded in 1922 by Grace and George Zambra and effectively closed in about 1961. The nursery was briefly resurrected from about 1980 to 1984, by one of the sisters then owning Windward, Mrs Jean Arnot, who with the help of her son and the encouragement of Roy Coombs, sold violets at home and abroad. The nursery is now in business for the third time, under Edmund Holden:

'Elsie Coombs'. White with an indigo eye. A sport of *V.o.* 'Rawson's White' found at Windward about 1978 by Roy Coombs and named in memory of his mother.

'Jean Arnot'. A deeper pink sport on the original plant of *V.o.* 'Princess Diana'.

'Mrs R. Barton'. Many white flowers with violet markings of variable intensity. Mrs Zambra wrote that this was a seedling of *V.o.* 'Princess of Wales' found in 1930; in their last price lists it is said that *V.o.* 'Alassio', which was imported from Italy in the 1920s or before, is a synonym of *V.o.* 'Mrs R. Barton'. Named after the foreman's wife.

'Norah Church'. Very early violet-mauve flowers. Claimed to have been found in the wild and introduced by Windward in 1930; but this may have been a cultivar raised at George Lee's nursery near Bristol before the Great War. Named after a friend of the Zambras.

'Opera'. Single lilac-mauve flowers with pale blue shading and a rose centre. Raised or introduced in about 1930.

'Pamela Zambra'. Large late violet-blue flowers, shading to purple, the scent elusive soon after picking. A seedling of *V.o.* 'Explorateur Dybowski', perhaps crossed with *V. septentrionalis* or *V. cucullata*, raised in about 1930 and named after the proprietor's daughter.

'Princess Diana'. A large vigorous pale pink violet found in the vegetable garden at Windward by Roy Coombs in about 1982.

'Windward'. The sweetly scented flowers are an unusual pale crimson-rose colour. A seedling of *V.o.* 'Admiral Avellan' found in 1945.

pedunculata. Californian Golden Violet or Yellow Pansy. Large yellow flowers with reddish-brown backs and short dark brown veins on the lower 3 petals. May. 4–12 in. (10–30 cm) high in flower. Rather tender; flowers in winter and spring in the wild, dying down for the summer and autumn drought. Discovered by David Douglas and introduced by William Lobb to Veitch in 1854.

Vitis vinifera 'Mrs Pince' (Vitaceae). See p.106.

BIBLIOGRAPHY

Books

Allwood, M. *Carnations for Everyone* (Blandford Press, 1953)

Anderson, E.B. *Seven Gardens* (Michael Joseph, 1973)

Bean, W.J. *Trees and Shrubs Hardy in the British Isles* 8th edition. 4 vol. & suppl. (John Murray, 1970–88)

Beckett, K. *Royal Horticultural Society Encyclopedia of House Plants* (Century, 1987)

Bloom, A. *Perennials for Trouble-free Gardening* (1960)

Bowles, E.A. *My Garden in Spring; Summer; Autumn & Winter* 3 vol. (T.C. & E.C. Jack, 1914–15)

Boullemier *Check-list of ... the genus Fuchsia* (Blandford Press, 1985)

Brickell, C. and Sharman, F. *The Vanishing Garden* (John Murray, 1986)

Briggs *The Flora of Plymouth* (Arbroath)

Bruggeman, L. *Tropical Plants and their cultivation* (Thames & Hudson, 1969)

Burkill, I.H. *A Dictionary of the Economic Products of the Malay Peninsula* (Crown Agents, 1935)

Coates, A. *Garden Shrubs and their histories* (Studio Vista, 1963)

———— *A Quest for Plants* (Studio Vista, 1969)

Coombs, R. *Violets: the History and Cultivation of Scented Violets* (Croom Helm, 1981)

Cory, R. *The Horticultural Record* (J. & A. Churchill, 1914)

Cox, P.A. and K. *The Encyclopedia of Rhododendron Hybrids* (Batsford, 1988)

Dartington Hall Gardens *Nursery Catalogue* (c.1934)

Day, A.R. and Michelmore, A.P.G. *Herbert Whitley and Primley House, Paignton* (Torbay Civic Society, 1987)

Druery, C.T. *British Ferns and their varieties* (Routledge)

Everard, B. and Morley, B. *Wild Flowers of the World* (Ebury Press & Michael Joseph, 1970)

Graf, A.B. *Exotica 3* 2 vol. (Rutherford, N.J., 1963)

———— *Tropica* 2nd edition (Rutherford, N.J., 1981)

Gorer, R. *Climbing Plants* (Faber, 1968)

———— *The Growth of Gardens* (Faber, 1978)

Grigson, G. *Englishman's Flora* (Paladin, 1958)

Hadfield, M. *A History of British Gardening* (Hamlyn, 1969)

———— *Pioneers in Gardening* (Routledge & Kegan Paul, 1955)

Harling, R. and Highton, L. *British Gardeners: a biographical dictionary* (A. Zwemmer, 1980)

Harris, T.Y. *Australian Plants for the Garden* (Sydney, 1953)

Harvey, J. *The Early Nurseries of Exeter* (Garden History Conference Notes, 1981, Exeter)

Haworth-Booth, M. *Effective Flowering Shrubs* (Collins, 1951)

———— *The Hydrangeas* (Constable, 1950)

Herklots, G. *Flowering Tropical Climbers* (Dawson, 1976)

Hillier, H.G. *Hillier's Manual of Trees and Shrubs* 5th edition (David & Charles, 1972)

Ingwersen, W. *Manual of Alpine Plants* (W. Ingwersen and Dunnsprint Ltd, 1978)

James, N.D.G. *The Trees of Bicton* (Blackwell, 1969)

Kaye, R. *Hardy Ferns* (Dent, 1968)

Krussmann, G. *Manual of Cultivated Broad-leaved Trees and Shrubs* 3 vol. (Batsford, 1985–6)

Lancaster, R. *Garden Plants for Connoisseurs* (Unwin Hyman, 1987)

Letts, J.F. *Hardy Heaths and the Heather Garden* (Letts, c.1965)

Menninger, E.A. *Flowering Vines of the World* (Heathside N.Y., 1970)

Millais, J.G. *Rhododendrons and the various hybrids* (Longmans, Green & Co., 1917)

Mitchell, A. *A Field Guide to the Trees of Britain* (Collins, 1974)

Nelson, E.C. *An Irish Flower Garden* (Boethius Press, Dublin, 1984)

Oldham, C.H. *The Cultivation of Berried Fruits* (C. Lockwood & Son, 1946)

The Plantfinder (Headmain Ltd, 1987)

Royal Horticultural Society *Dictionary of Gardening* 4 vol. & suppl. 2nd edition (Clarendon Press, 1984)

Roach, F.A. *Cultivated Fruits of Britain* (Basil Blackwell, 1985)

Robinson, W. *Flora and Silva* 3 vol. (1903–05)

Schmidt, M.G. *Growing Californian Native Plants* (University of California Press, 1980)

Smith, A.W. *A Gardener's Dictionary of Plant Names* Revised by W.T. Stearn (Cassell, 1972)

Synge, P.M. *The Gardens of Britain: I. Devon & Cornwall* (Batsford, 1977)

Taylor, H.V. *The Apples of England* (Crosby, Lockwood, 1948)

——— *The Plums of England* (Crosby, Lockwood, 1948)

Thomas, G.S. *Perennial Garden Plants* 2nd edition (Dent, 1982)

Treseder, N. *Magnolias* (Faber, 1978)

Underhill, T. *Heaths and Heathers* (David & Charles, 1971)

Veitch, J.H. *Hortus Veitchii* (James Veitch & Sons, 1906)

Ward, F. Kingdon. *Berried Treasure* (Ward Lock, 1954)

——— *Pilgrimage for Plants* (Harrap, 1960)

Warburton, B. *The World of Iris*

Willis, J.C. *A Dictionary of the Flowering Plants and Ferns* 7th edition (Cambridge University Press, 1966)

Zambra, G.L. *Violets for Garden and Market* (Collingridge, 1950)

Periodicals and journals

National Council for the Conservation of Plants & Gardens *Newsletter* (National). 1982, no. 1–

——— (Devon Group) *Newsletter* 1981, no. 1–

Alpine Garden Society *Bulletin* 1930–

Amateur Gardening 1906

The British Fern Gazette 1909 vol. 1–

The Daffodil and Tulip Yearbook 1981 (RHS)

Devonshire Association *Transactions*, vol. XCII, XCIV (J. Caldwell)

Exeter Flying-Post Various numbers

The Floricultural Cabinet vol. 1–

The Florists' Journal vol. 1–

The Fuchsia Annual 1939, 1941–52

The Gardeners' Chronicle 1841–

Index Kewensis vol. 1–2, suppl. 1985

Journal of Horticulture: Cottage Gardener and Country Gentleman 1863–6

The New Flora and Silva 1929–40

The Plantsman vol. 1–

The Pteridologist 1984 vol. 1–

Royal Horticultural Society *Journal* continued as *The Garden* 1866–

——— *Extracts from the Proceedings* and *Wisley Trial Reports*

The Rhododendron Handbook pt 1. P.M. Synge (RHS, 1967)

Specific articles

The British Fern Gazette 1915, vol. III, pp. 45–8, 'The Romance of Lady Clarissima'

Cornwall Garden Society Journal Mar. 1987, Heriz-Smith: 'Short History of … the brothers, William and Thomas Lobb'

Country Life 14 Mar. 1985, Heriz-Smith: 'A Keen Eye and a Lion's Heart: Richard Pearce'

Garden History: the Journal of the Garden History Society, Spring and Autumn 1988, Heriz-Smith: 'The Veitch Nurseries of Killerton and Exeter, 1780-1863'

ACKNOWLEDGEMENTS

Paintings

Mrs Yvonne Matthews
Mrs Rosanne Sanders

Line Drawings

Mrs Sri Kartawiada

Organizations
Bicton College of Agriculture
British Pteridological Society
City of Plymouth Civic Centre
City of Plymouth Parks Department
Dartington Hall Library
Devon County Library – Ivybridge Mobile Van
Forestry Commission – Westonbirt Arboretum
Herbert Whitley Trust Library
Lindley Library (Mr Brent Elliot and Miss Howell)
The National Trust
University of Exeter

Individuals

Mr K.W.H. Adlam
Lady Amory
Mrs Arbuthnot
the Argles family
Mrs J. Arnot
Mr K. Ashburner
Mr A.J.R. Bailey
Mr H. Baker
Miss Barnard
Mrs M. Bartlett
Mr & Mrs H.E. Bawden
Mrs Benger
Mrs H. Booker
Mr & Mrs R. Bowden
Mr C. Brickell
Miss F.S. Burgoyne
Mr J.R.L. Carter
Sir Charles Cave, Bart.
Mr R. Cheek
Mr D. Chalk
Mr D. Clarke
Mr P. Coates
Mr F. Collett
Mr R. Coombs
Mr F.C. Cornwell
Mrs S. Court
Mr A. Crouch
Mr K. Croucher
Mr D. Donald

Mr M. Feesey
Mr G. Ford
Mr B. Fretwell
Mr R. Fulcher
Mr J. Furze
Mr G. Gammin
Mr D.S. Gardham
Mr J. Gardiner
Mr A. Godfrey
Mrs P. Gossage
Mr G. Haddow
Mr P. Hall
Mrs G. Hatch
Mr & Mrs M. Henry
Mrs S. Heriz-Smith
Mr A. Hicks
Mr M. Hickson
Mr F. Holden
Mr & Mrs F.J. Holmes
Mr & Mrs R. Hubbard
Mr C. Jermy
Mr T. Jones
Mr R. Lancaster
Mr N. Langdon
Mr F. Lavin
Surg. Capt. Lock R.N.
Mr P. Lower
Mr N. Lucas
Mr H.B. Luscombe

Major W. Magor
Mrs Marker
Mrs Y. Matthews
Mrs D. McLennan
Mr H. Mellor
Mr Miller
Mr A. Mitchell
Mrs C.A. Morris
Mr B. Mousley
Mr A. G. Murdoch
Mrs J. Nash
Dr E.C. Nelson
Mr R.D. Nutt
The Lady Anne Palmer
Mr S. Pawlowski
Mr M. Pharoah
Mr A. Phull
Mrs F. Pickard
Miss M. Pickthorne
Mrs B. Pinnock
Dr A. Plack
Mr J. Platt
Miss J. Primmer
Mr & Mrs H. Read
Major R.A.W. Reynolds
Mr B. & Miss W.
Rittershausen
Lady Roborough
Mrs M. Rogerson

Mr D.J.T. Rose
Mr S. Scarr
Mrs J. Shackleton
Mr H. Sharp
Mr M. Simmons
Lady Skelmersdale
Dr J. Smart
Mr & Mrs M. Squires
Mr B.N. Starling
Dr G.S. Steele-Perkins
Miss E. Strangman
Dr T.D.V. Swinscow
Mr M. Taylor
Mr G.S. Thomas
Mrs P. Thompson
Mr N. Timpson
Dr A.G. Touch
Mr T. Underhill
Mr R. Waite
Mr C. Warner
Mrs I. Webb
Mr H.J. Welch
Mr J. Whetman
Mrs J. Wilder
Mr & Mrs K. Wiley
Mr C. Willing
Dr D. Wilson
Mr J. Wright
Mr T. Wright
Mrs V. Wyatt

Photographic Team

Mrs H. Booker
Mr P. Bowles

Mrs A. Kingdon
Mr J. Lloyd

Mrs F. Pickard
Miss J. Primmer

Mr M. Russell
Mr M. Squires

And our thanks to all those who have kindly allowed us to photograph their plants, or who have so generously lent us slides.

The quotation from Gertrude Jekyll's *Wood and Garden* is reproduced by courtesy of The Antique Collectors' Club.

INDEX